Prese   ın

of
College Biology Teachers:
A Search For A Better Way

DONALD S. DEAN
Staff Biologist

November, 1970

Published by the
Commission on Undergraduate Education
in the Biological Sciences

Supported by a grant from the
National Science Foundation to the
American Institute of Biological Sciences

Copies of this report are available
free of charge from
THE COMMISSION ON UNDERGRADUATE
EDUCATION IN THE BIOLOGICAL SCIENCES
3900 Wisconsin Avenue, N.W.
Washington,. D.C. 20016

COMMISSION ON UNDERGRADUATE EDUCATION IN THE BIOLOGICAL SCIENCES

Commission Members (as of July 1970)

Chairman
JERRY J. KOLLROS
University of Iowa

Vice Chairman
JAMES T. ROBINSON
BSCS
University of Colorado

RICHARD G. BEIDLEMAN
Colorado College

JAMES M. BENNETT
New York University

CHARLES R. BOTTICELLI
Boston University

THOMAS A. COLE
Wabash College

RICHARD A. DODGE
Columbia Junior College

HAROLD E. FINLEY
Howard University

SIDNEY W. FOX
University of Miami

LAFAYETTE FREDERICK
Atlanta University

GEORGE A. GRIES
Oklahoma State University

JOHNS W. HOPKINS, III
Washington University

ROBERT W. LONG
University of South Florida

HOPE RITTER, JR.
University of Georgia

ANTHONY SAN PIETRO
Indiana University

HELEN STAFFORD
Reed College

E. PETER VOLPE
Tulane University

VAL WOODWARD
University of Minnesota

Ex-Officio

GEORGE L. McNEW
President, AIBS

EDWARD J. KORMONDY
Director, CUEBS

STANFORD MOORE
President, FASEB

Executive Office Staff

EDWARD J. KORMONDY
Director

DANA L. ABELL
Senior Staff Biologist

JOAN G. CREAGER
Staff Biologist

DONALD S. DEAN
Staff Biologist

DARREL L. MURRAY
Staff Biologist

JOHN D. WITHERS
Staff Biologist

Contents

Foreword

Teaching and learning: these are on opposite sides of the coin of human survival. As there are self-learners, there are born teachers: these survive or ensure survival. But for others on the learning end, the capacity to cope with life's challenges is increased by the skill of the teacher in transmitting the lessons of the past. The challenge, then, in matters educational, is to identify those skills of the effective teacher and to cultivate them in those susceptible to improvement. In no small measure, that is what this publication, the fruition of a substantial CUEBS project, is about.

Charged as it was with the task of improving undergraduate education in biology, CUEBS addressed itself to the tangibles: to the content and organization of the curriculum, to the nature and extent of laboratory facilities and library resources. But, from the very start, the Commission recognized that people, not things, were the critical cog in the process, that teachers were most often the actual deterrent to CUEBS' purpose. It was also recognized that getting a handle on this problem was elusive, and that this was a kind of *sanctum sanctorum* of graduate education. If CUEBS were to have had respect for sacred cows from its inception, however, it would have had no business being in business at all.

Early efforts by the Panel on College Instructional Personnel[1] were significant not so much in tangible product as in aiding the erosion of the mortar of professional resistance and reluctance, using the chinking to pave the way for this past year's work. The concatenation of student, parental, legislative, and other demands for better teaching coincided with a growing movement on the part of the academic community itself to do a better job. CUEBS was able to capitalize on this

---

[1] Members of the Panel at various times, and their present addresses: Lewis E. Anderson, (Duke University) ; Gerald A. Cole, (Arizona State University) ; Rezneat M. Darnell, (Texas A&M University) ; Richard Garth, (University of Tennessee at Chattanooga) ; Artis P. Graves, (Agricultural and Technical College of North Carolina) ; Donald Humphrey, (Evergreen State College) ; Willis H. Johnson, (Wabash College) ; Robert MacVicar, (Southern Illinois University) ; Lewis N. Pino, (Oakland University) ; Martin W. Schein, (West Virginia University) ; Grover Stephens, (University of California at Irvine) ; William K. Stephenson, (Earlham College) ; Sanford S. Tepfer, (University of Oregon) ; Charles S. Thornton, (Michigan State University) ; Charles M. Vaughn, (Miami University) ; Allyn J. Watterman, (National Institute for Child Health and Development) ; Donald Wise, (College of Wooster) ; Newell Younggren, (University of Arizona) .

rising interest rate and to take advantage of both the near universal concern and the halting corrective steps some institutions were taking.

But, CUEBS is people; it is Commissioners, past and present, and staff, past and present. In reality, it is the whole biological community that works with Commissioners and staff to bring improvement to biological education. On the nitty gritty day-by-day basis of getting a job done, however, responsibility falls to a single individual. In this case, the Commission, in the largest sense of all its "members," owes an immeasurable debt of gratitude to Donald S. Dean who commandeered the forces requisite to getting the job done. His effort is reflected not only in this publication but in the diverse responses occurring in many graduate departments as a result of the conference program he directed.

To Don Dean, to the participants of the conferences described in this report, to the Commission which has continually supported and encouraged this project, I express a word of gratitude—not from me but on behalf of future students whose instruction will be better as a result of these efforts.

EDWARD J. KORMONDY
Director, CUEBS
September, 1970

Preface

The time is now! All over the country those concerned with the preparation of college biology teachers are asking this question: How can this be done better? Graduate students and foundations are asking; so are faculty members and administrators. Those who appoint faculty members and those who will be taught by them are asking. The question is no longer *whether* preparation of college biology teachers should be improved but *how*. It was in response to this call that CUEBS developed the program reported here.

It has been exciting to participate in this effort at a time when the issue is so vital and so many are anxiously seeking answers. A surfer must have the same feeling when he catches the big wave at just the right time.

The big difference is that surfing is a solitary contest between the surfer and the sea; the movement to prepare better college teachers is not. Hundreds of busy and able people participated in this CUEBS endeavor. The generosity, camaraderie, and high purpose of those who worked together to further the cause added an extra dimension—an intensely human quality. It is hard to describe the warmth of feeling that comes from working with people of such stature on something so important.

Ann Heiss, Frank Koen, and Robert Koenker supplied the provocative literature to start the action. Erich Steiner, Stanford Erickson, Ann Heiss, W. M. Laetsch, Fred Reif, Leonard Machlis, Edward Hodgson, and Langley Wood helped plan the conferences and, through their own interest and example, enlisted the support of others.

The programs of the CUEBS conferences have been placed in the appendix of this volume so that those who gave the thoughtful talks, participated in panel discussions, and directed working groups can be noted. Those who shared ideas as participants are also listed. It would be well worth the effort to see who these people were. We hope they will realize how grateful we are for their participation.

Dr. Frank Koen of the Center for Research on Learning and Teaching of the University of Michigan has become an authority on the development of programs for making the teaching assistant program a learning experience. It seemed particularly appropriate to have him write Chapter 2 on the teaching assistant.

The splendid hospitality of the University of Michigan, the University of California at Berkeley, and the New England Center for Continuing Education added much to the success of the conferences.

Finally, we gratefully acknowledge the unfailing support of the Commission and the professional staff of CUEBS and AIBS. It should also be noted that the preparation of college teachers has been a concern of CUEBS since its inception.

Let us hope that all who have shared in this effort will receive the ultimate reward—seeing an improvement in the preparation of teachers as a consequence of their endeavors.

DONALD S. DEAN

1. In Search
of a Better Way

The university has two major functions: the discovery of knowledge and the dissemination of knowledge. It is generally agreed that the research performance of American universities is discharged with distinction, but it would be hard to find someone who would claim that the teaching function is characterized by equal quality.

One consideration makes any neglect of teaching particularly serious: the university is almost the only place where one can earn the credentials to become a college teacher. If the university fails to produce graduates prepared to do a creditable job of college teaching, the inadequacy is reinforced in an endless cycle of poor performance. This publication is designed to explore the ways to correct that cycle of mediocrity. We at CUEBS are particularly concerned with the preparation of college biology teachers, but much that is said could also be said of any other discipline.

Recently, the public has been made acutely conscious of the inadequacies of undergraduate education. It is time to attack the problem at its roots—the preparation of the college teacher. Work with curriculum, laboratories, facilities, and bibliography may be a waste of time without the essential ingredient: a creative college teacher. This is not to except blames which can be cast on the prior preparation of the student and the motivation he brings to the classroom. Nonetheless, the critical factor is in all instances that teacher who can obviate those disconcerting factors.

It should be emphasized that the expression used was "a creative college teacher," not a person who has had a specified number of courses in the art of teaching. It is certainly not our purpose to urge neglect of the scholarly function of the university, for it is hard to inculcate a zest for inquiry unless one has experienced zestful inquiry. It is unlikely that one who does not know biology well will teach it well. In the words of one panelist at a CUEBS conference:

> Caring about people may be an essential point of departure for good teaching but it certainly is not the basis for a lifelong career until it has been buttressed by a little something in the way of scholarship.[1]

---

[1] Dr. Laura Bornholdt, Vice-President of the Danforth Foundation, at the New England conference.

I

Let us suggest a definition of an ideal college teacher to avoid any misunderstanding of the goal. No one will achieve this ideal in fullest measure, but a program to improve the preparation of college teachers must have direction. A person planning to teach in college might well aspire to being a teacher with these characteristics:

He knows first-hand what it means to probe the farthest reaches of our knowledge and to add some new light to our darkness.

He sees the whole sweep of biology and sees it in all of its intricate pattern and dynamic interaction.

For him biology is a nodal point in the whole pattern of human concerns. The chemistry, physics, mathematics, philosophy, psychology, literature, art, and history of living things are important to him.

He cares and cares passionately about other people. Sharing the adventure of learning and guiding the learning of others are a source of deep satisfaction to him—not just a source of income.

He has the creative urge and imagination that distinguishes a great researcher from a hack and finds a major outlet for his talents in seeking a better way to teach.

He reads widely out of habit. To him, life is a never-ending inquiry.

He has acquired some skill in teaching and some confidence in his ability. He has some knowledge of what goals are worthy and what methods are helpful. He knows that the refinement of his skills as a teacher is a life-long quest.

Finally, his efforts support the efforts of his fellow teachers. No pettiness of spirit or shabby ethical standards choke the progress of the common endeavor.

There are those who say that teachers are born: if one is fated by some happy combination of genes and environment to be a good teacher nothing will thwart him. If he lacks the innate talent to be a teacher, no instruction will make the slightest difference.

Maybe so, but it is difficult to believe that we whose business is education should put so little faith in the value of education as to suppose that a person cannot improve his ability to handle the complexities of teaching. This volume is written on the assumption that better college teachers can be and should be produced.

Questions are being asked by a lot of people today: undergraduates are questioning, as never before, the quality and relevance of their education; graduate students express chagrin and embarrassment that they as teaching assistants are not providing the undergraduates as good an education as they should get; foundations are asking whether the money spent to improve education is achieving the goals set. As dislocations of supply and demand occur consequent to the recent slashes in research funds, departments at teaching institutions will have an opportunity to exercise greater discrimination in selecting faculty. Administrators and faculty members in many institutions are asking themselves some hard questions about their responsibilities. The rapid rise of developing universities and the shocks and rude challenges to the routine procedure have caused some serious introspection.

No one can guess the shape of the future, but anyone with any awareness of the world today knows that tomorrow will be vastly different. Many of tomorrow's college teachers are in graduate schools today; the question is what to do about this fact.

It would have a salutory effect if the heads of departments of biology in graduate schools were to ask themselves the no-nonsense questions listed below. If they were then to ask responsible members of the administration the same questions, so much the better. It would take more courage, but some of the most meaningful answers would probably come from very recent graduates who are presently teaching in college and from graduate students presently teaching in the university. They should be consulted.

1. Is it true that research and teaching are twin responsibilities of your department?

   Is your performance equally distinguished in both areas?

   If you are only concerned with research, do you make this clear in your literature so that those who plan to make a career of college teaching will be directed elsewhere?

2. If your freshmen are taught by teaching assistants, are you proud of the education they receive?

   Would *you* want to take the freshman course?

   Would you be pleased to have the academic reputation of the university depend upon the beginning course?

   Does your beginning course have input from your best faculty talent to make it an outstanding course?

   Are your teaching assistants selected for their interest and ability and do you give them the support, supervision, and instruction needed to do a good job of teaching?

3. Is the teaching experience a learning experience for teaching assistants or is the arrangement an inexpensive expedient for handling the crowd?

Could the experience be made more instructive?

Does the experience attract the resourceful, bright graduate students?

Do TAs receive instruction and orientation?

Is the experience set in a context of learning; does it make use of what is known about teaching?

Are teaching assistants well supervised and do they have a place to turn for criticism and guidance?

Do they have a chance to do more than perform a service?

Do they have a chance to teach at various levels and use various techniques: lecture, discussion group, laboratory, etc. Is there a chance to create something original?

4. Are you proud of the teaching performance of your alumni?

5. If you accept NDEA fellows or others receiving support to be better teachers, do you have a program to merit such support?

6. How do you feel about other degrees?

Should you offer a Doctor of Arts or some other practitioner's degree?

Should there be opportunity within your Ph.D. program to prepare college teachers of whom you will be proud?

7. Does the administration honor the university's dual commitment: research and teaching?

In accepting responsibility as the teachers of teachers, graduate institutions assume accountability for the most sensitive aspects of the whole educational effort.

DR. ANN M. HEISS
Univerity of California, Berkeley
Berkeley Conference

Only those intimately involved with these questions at the university will know all of the answers, but we at CUEBS know what some will answer. At many institutions, honest efforts are being made to decide upon an honorable course and to implement it—no easy matter—for the problems of preparing better college teachers are deeply enmeshed in the very nature of American higher education.

One fundamental characteristic which chokes off progress toward better teaching and better teacher preparation is the fact that teaching does not command the respect and support accorded research.[2] The outstanding researcher commands respect because he has been able to build the reputation of the institution, to attract the brightest people, and to do the exciting things. Through his grant support, he has been able to pay the grocer, so to speak, and the breadwinner always wins respect. A graduate student would not have to be too discerning to know that the rewards—not only material rewards but the stirring intellectual rewards—are presently found most quickly in research. Dr. Joseph Ramus, now at Yale University, put the hard question at the Washington CUEBS conference:

> Preservice training is admirable and necessary, but it serves only to cure the symptoms, not the disease. The reason undergraduate training is neglected is that it is a ticket to a lesser institution. Is CUEBS prepared to address itself to this anachronism in American college and univerity education?

Too often the educational component has merely been a dutiful service; "There is a job to do; let's get it done the best way we can under the circumstances and get on with the exciting part." Happily, there are those who have discovered in college teaching a demanding and stimulating challenge. They recognize it as one of the most complex problems imaginable and one of the most critical social responsibilities of our time. Some find it a challenge worthy of the finest minds and find great satisfaction in attacking the problems of education.

Some have accepted this challenge despite the current fashion in university circles, but the easiest course has been to accommodate to the prevailing reward system. It is no small matter for a department to produce an *ideal* program for preparation of college teachers in a *real* and imperfect world. The efforts of those who try should not be disparaged.

In some cases, however, one listens to what is done about the preparation of college biology teachers with a mixture of amazed disbelief and sodden despair:

> Can it be that a distinguished university would put a man in charge of the beginning biology course because it did not trust him to do anything it thought to be more important?

> Is it really possible that another distinguished university chooses its teaching assistants from foreign nationals and Americans with

---

[2] One of the best analyses of this point is found in the works of Dr. Ann M. Heiss of the Center of Research and Development in Higher Education, University of California, Berkeley. Her paper *The Preparation of College and University Teachers* is particularly relevant.

weaker academic credentials because it has been unable to get any other kind of support?

Can a teaching assistant honestly say that there was no person he could turn to for guidance in how to handle his section?

Are undergraduate institutions really willing to hire a new Ph.D. who has had virtually no zoology to teach their beginning biology courses?

Can it be that at an institution which advertises its concern for preparing college teachers there is only one man with a professed interest in the subject and when he is on leave there is no faculty member, administrator, or graduate student to attend a conference on the subject?

In some cases, the answer is yes. While one must resist falling into the trap of sitting about recounting horror stories and shocking anecdotes, one had best not ignore the fact that few are satisfied with the general performance in preparing future college biology teachers. We must give serious thought to the consequences of allowing business as usual to prevent a change of direction.

I am currently a graduate student completing the Ph.D. I have just accepted a position for next September teaching a two-term non-major biology course. I would appreciate any help which you could give me in the planning of this course.

I am relatively a little weak in physiology and very weak in zoology. I would therefore especially appreciate any help you could offer in the latter areas.

Letter to AIBS
Office of Biological Education

Dr. Laura Bornholdt said at the New England conference of CUEBS:

Something has to give. It is possible that American higher education is approaching a watershed in the preparation of university teachers. Dissatisfaction with the old concept of let-them-learn-the-way-I-did is matched by scorn for the result.

Earlier in this chapter, faculty, administration, graduate students, and alumni were urged to think through their role in response to some hard-nosed questions. They must all contribute to the effort to plot a course of action if it is to succeed.

At CUEBS we have taken a firm stand on one point: the preparation of college biology teachers will not improve without the very finest effort from faculty, department heads, graduate students, administrators, yes, and officials of foundations, government agencies, and the employers of graduates. All have a common interest in the success of the effort: if it succeeds, all profit; if it drags along at a level unworthy of pride, all lose. Each depends upon the other and an adversary role, encouraged by an outside agency, is more likely to exacerbate the problem than produce a solution.

At the CUEBS conferences held this year, all of these groups have been represented. Graduate students can be proud of their bright, articulate, thoughtful, responsible colleagues who attended and made their contribution. Faculty and administrators were sincerely searching for a way. It would seem likely that if all faculty members and administrators were as intelligently concerned about the preparation of college biology teachers as those who attended the CUEBS conferences there would soon be no need for such conferences.

CUEBS INVOLVEMENT

From its inception in 1963, CUEBS has been involved in a serious effort to upgrade the preparation of college biology teachers. For most of the lifetime of CUEBS, a subpanel was concerned with the problem and wrestled with ways to change the situation. In 1968, Humphrey and Wise prepared a paper which is quoted elsewhere in this work. In the same year, CUEBS solicited a series of papers describing model seminars to improve preparation of college teachers. In May 1969, a national conference at Michigan State University brought together those who were known to be doing something significant about preparing their future teachers.

The CUEBS effort in 1969-70 has all been of one fabric. It began with delineation of the problem at a conference in Washington in September. The three subsequent conferences were devoted to a serious effort to finding solutions. Those at the Washington conference said, "We learned so much—but how few heard this." Some at the conference—including graduate students—rushed home and started action on their own campuses, asking: What can be done?[3] CUEBS decided to get closer to the universities of the country by holding regional conferences so that more people could get involved, so that natural groups of concerned people would get to know who else cares and perhaps develop mutually supporting activities. The conferences were held at the University of Michigan, University of California at Berkeley, and the New England Center for Continuing Education on the campus of the University of New Hampshire. About two-thirds of the nation's supply of Ph.D. biologists are graduated from the uni-

---

[3] See the program of a forum organized by a graduate student, John Jungck, in Appendix H.

versities represented at one or more of the CUEBS conferences on the preparation of college biology teachers. Unfortunately, it was not possible to hold conferences in other regions.

THE WASHINGTON CONFERENCE: DELINEATION OF THE PROBLEM

At this conference, 14 recent graduates with brand-new Ph.D. degrees who had taught for one year, 9 graduate students, and 14 department heads, foundation officials, and faculty members were brought together to define the problem.

The most memorable part of the conference was a panel by the new faculty members who had just completed their first year of teaching. First, they were asked what they did in their initial year, then each was asked what preparation he had had for doing a good job during that first year. They told it straight. They praised the worthwhile aspects of their preparation (mostly the academic preparation), they were understanding of the magnitude of the problem, and they were equally straightforward about the deficiencies of the program. Their responses came from both the heart and the head.

The low esteem in which the teaching function of the university is held was indicted as the major source of the problem.

> A lot of graduate faculty have a very negative attitude toward undergraduate teaching: if you can't do research, if you don't want to go into the big time, you can always teach undergraduates in a four-year college.

The poor quality of the teaching assistant experience came in for its share of criticism.

> Teaching assistants all too often become flunkies and not teaching assistants at all. It is almost a misnomer.

> As graduate students we taught courses that were cut and dried . . . as a new faculty member I am confronted with preparing my own course—it is mine, my course, my baby.

Implicit in the discussions at the conference were these basic ideas:

1. It is in the interest of the university to prepare good teachers, for the university is both the producer of college teachers and an employer of the product. Inadequately prepared teachers appointed to prepare other teachers perpetuate the inadequacy.

2. Universities have a similar responsibility to prepare good teachers for staffing two-year and four-year colleges. There is presently no other place where this can be done on an organized basis. It is difficult to see how this responsibility can be shrugged off.

3. Most preparation of college biology teachers is through the teaching assistant program. To the extent that the preparation is less than adequate, the university fails to keep faith with its own *graduate* students.

4. To the extent that undergraduate classes are taught by poorly trained and poorly supervised teaching assistants, the university fails to keep faith with its *undergraduate* students. The quality of undergraduate education is currently criticized by voices too loud to ignore.

Yeoman service as a teacher on most university faculties is a singular path to academic suicide.

Dr. Joseph S. Ramus
Yale University
Washington Conference

Recent graduates and graduate students felt a great need to experience a broad spectrum of the activities to be expected of them as teachers. Amost none had had experience in lecturing, educational planning, development of new laboratory experiences, or even in preparation and ordering of materials.

They found opportunity for involvement in the courses inadequate and they would have appreciated supervision, criticism, and a chance to grow professionally as teachers. Several spoke of being given an outline of the laboratory and being abandoned—with no one to give consistent supervision or help.

Those going to four-year colleges reported that they had not truly known what was expected of a faculty member at a college. Suggestions for correcting this situation were made.

It was agreed that learning to teach is done best in the context of a real situation, not by a didactic study of education. Thus, the teaching experience under supervision was thought to be the best way to prepare college biology teachers. Participants acknowledged the responsibility of others—including undergraduate institutions and hiring institutions—but placed primary responsibility for the education of future teachers with the graduate department.

It was generally agreed that there is no one best way to improve supervised teaching, that various approaches suited to local circumstances could be successful.

Students urged that discussion of the matter reach a greater audience, particularly among those not presently in contact with CUEBS activities. They spoke specifically of the need to communicate with graduate students.

There was widespread acceptance of the idea that the situation is not presently satisfactory and that it will not change until teaching is thought to be important.

Faculty and graduate students left the conference with new respect for each other and with a reinforced feeling that something must be done.

Our chairman is a fantastically busy man . . . . He has his problems, too.

Recent Graduate student
Washington Conference

REGIONAL CONFERENCES: THE SEARCH FOR ANSWERS

In setting up the regional conferences in response to the challenge of the new college teachers at the Washington meeting, a special effort was made to invite those who were likely to make a significant contribution. People at universities with graduate programs were asked for help in choosing the faculty member, graduate student, or administrator most concerned and most likely to make a difference. They chose well. (See Appendix G for a list of those who attended.)

At the three conferences, the time was spent on a search for a solution to the problems raised in Washington, not in rediscovering the problem. The programs of the conferences in Appendix F will show that much time was spent on the teaching assistant, for much of the preparation of graduate students as future college teachers involves on-the-job training of those presently teaching biology. At the Ann Arbor conference, the fact that the *future* teacher is *presently* a teacher was made particularly clear when Alfred Sussman said that of the credits earned by freshmen and sophomores at the University of Michigan, two-thirds are placed in classes taught by teaching fellows. This is probably not atypical.

At all of the conferences, ideas for improving the teaching assistant program were exchanged. Dr. Steiner, Dean Knight, Dr. Heiss, and Dr. Koen spoke on the subject.

Of 1843 people granted Ph.D.'s in biological fields by 94 leading universities in the period 1963–1967:
  — 69% became college teachers of biology
  — of these, 73% taught a beginning course.
Of these 94 universities:
  — 66% provided no special training to teaching assistants before they taught.
  — 80% offered no special course or seminar in any aspect of college teaching.

Unpublished report by Donald Humphrey and Donald Wise for a subpanel of the CUEBS Panel on College Instructional Personnel, 1968.

Alternatives to the Ph.D. were discussed at all of the conferences, and the presentation in Chapter 3 reflects these discussions. An interesting feature of the New England meeting was a panel on the subject of foundation support for the preparation of better college biology teachers with representatives from the National Science Foundation, the U.S. Office of Education, and the Danforth Foundation. It was emphasized that the public foundations intend to take an active role in guaranteeing quality in preparation of college teachers. It seems that they are no longer willing to write a blank check to support a program of teacher preparation without assurance that it is worthy. Dr. Lawrence Friedrich of the U.S. Office of Education said:

> The NDEA Title IV fellowship program was set up to train students working for the Ph.D., or its equivalent, who intend to become college teachers. During most of the history of the program the Office of Education assumed that universities would do whatever is necessary to prepare its Ph.D. students for college teaching. However, in most institutions nothing special has been done. . . .
>
> The Office of Education is now taking the stand that, though a university department may have a fine research faculty, if it does not provide a satisfactory program of training in college teaching for its Ph.D. students, it should not be awarded NDEA Title IV fellowships since the university is not meeting the major objective of the Title IV program—that of training teachers for colleges and universities.

Dr. Alfred Borg, Deputy Director, Division of Undergraduate Education in Science, National Science Foundation, was especially active at the conferences. He used reactions of the participants as feedback in developing ideas on how best to encourage the most creative scientists to use some of their talents to improve the teaching of science. It is very possible that the National Science Foundation will develop a program of prestigious National Science Professorships as one way to modify the reward system in graduate schools.

Other topics such as the role of research in the preparation of college teachers, technological aids to education, meeting the needs of the two-year and four-year institution, and a cooperative internship program were given attention at one or more of the conferences.

It is interesting to note that the human aspect of college teacher preparation came up again and again. Alfred Sussman, in his welcoming address at the Michigan Conference, pleaded for attention to the difficult problems of instilling the all-important inner qualities of a truly excellent teacher, including ethical and moral strength. Dean Knight, quoting Eric Fromm at the Berkeley Conference, warned that "while we learn knowledge, we are losing that teaching which is the most important one for human development: the teaching which can only be given by the simple presence of a mature, loving person."

These echo the concern expressed at the meetings and in answers to questionnaires that gimmicks and gadgets and instant solutions are no substitute for a worthy exemplar, for a chance to be a colleague working on an important problem, and for the attention of a warm-blooded human being who cares.

Since a large number of the institutions preparing college biology teachers were represented at one conference or another, a major function was served in bringing together concerned people in a situation which ensured exchange of ideas. Much that will be accomplished will not find expression in print but in the changes brought about on campuses when the participants, encouraged and enforced by the discovery that others care, put their ideas into practice.

Nonetheless, the influence of the conference can be increased by publications. Since the conferences were intended to be action-oriented, some of the most current ideas discussed at the conferences are set forth here in the form of recommendations. As listed, they are not the specific parliamentary action of participants and speakers at the CUEBS conferences, but they are strongly influenced by the discussions at the meetings and recommendations prepared there.

RECOMMENDATIONS TO GRADUATE SCHOOLS

1. Give thought to the desirability of a Doctor of Arts degree or other practitioner's degree. Alternatively, consider how the needs of those who will teach in colleges and universities can be met better within the framework of the Ph.D. degree. (See Chapters 3 and 5)

2. Permit truly creative investigation related to the teaching of biology to be used in appropriate cases as a dissertation. (See Chapters 3 and 5)

3. Consider the suggestions presented for improving the program for teaching assistants. (See Chapters 2 and 4 and Appendix A)

4. Organize a fall conference on teaching for teaching assistants and staff. Consider an interdepartmental effort. (See Chapter 4 and Appendix B)

5. Consider developing a seminar or course on effective teaching as a companion to the teaching experience. (See Chapter 2 and Appendices C and D)

6. Develop with undergraduate institutions a plan for a cooperative internship. (See Chapters 4, 5, and 6)

7. Explore ways to improve the status and dignity of the teaching assistant. Explore ways to improve his sense of participation and colleagueship. (See Chapter 2 and Appendix A)

8. Examine the programs of the graduate students to see whether they provide these:

Adequate breadth of preparation for college teaching (and for research) .

Research activities realistically related to the students' plans for the future so that they will not give up research as soon as the resources of the university are no longer available.

The initiation of a life-long program of professional reading and professional growth. (See Chapter 5)

9. Review your program for NDEA fellows to see whether it fills the need. (See report of the New England Conference)

10. Find ways to enlist the participation of senior members of the department in the improvement of the program for future teachers. Consider the appointment of a department coordinator of college-teacher preparation. (See Chapter 4)

11. Propose to NSF or other foundations a plan for support of a person of proven creativity and ability who wants to apply his talents to developing an original contribution to the teaching of biology.

12. Include the teaching performance of faculty as one criterion for advancement. (See Chapter 1)

RECOMMENDATIONS TO HIRING INSTITUTIONS

1. Appoint teaching staff for the specific qualities and preparation desired rather than the prestige of a particular degree alone. Give serious thought to what these qualities and this preparation should be, and make your wishes known to the universities. (See Chapters 2, 3, and 5)

2. Make sure that a new appointee knows exactly what is expected of him and what support he can expect. Take responsibility for giving the new teacher a chance to get started well and to continue a program of growth throughout his career. (See Chapter 5)

If teaching and the whole educational process are to get the attention they deserve from creative people, then teaching must be made competitive with research in terms of the rewards it brings.

DR. ALFRED S. BORG, NSF
Berkeley Conference

2. The Preparation of College Teachers

FRANK KOEN

University of Michigan

In many large universities, as many as one-third of the credit hours earned by undergraduates are taken in classes taught, for all practical purposes, by graduate student teaching assistants. Despite the hue and cry that sometimes attends this fact, there is little objective evidence that undergraduates are being educationally short-changed by this arrangement. The changes rest on the assumption that these less experienced and less knowledgeable individuals must, perforce, be less effective teachers than degree-holding faculty. But relatively few of today's university faculty members have received any systematic guidance in the acquisition of instructional skills. Virtually their only opportunity for learning something about teaching before the attainment of the doctoral degree was the teaching assistantship. In an environment which prizes personal scholarship above all else, however, the teaching assistantship is most often viewed as an activity whose main effect is to slow down the attainment of the degree. We now have nationally funded programs whose stated objective is to reduce the time interval between the baccalaureate and doctorate degrees. It is interesting to note that the existence of such programs is most commonly interpreted to call for the reduction or elimination of service by the graduate student as a teaching assistant, the best opportunity that most graduate students will ever have for learning teaching crafts and strategies. The short-sightedness of such a policy becomes startlingly clear when one reflects on the fact that about 50% of the recipients of the Ph.D. will do some college teaching, with the percentage ranging from a low of 25% in the natural sciences to virtually 100% in the humanities. Thus, the effect is to facilitate the attainment of a degree which will permit one to obtain a faculty appointment while minimizing preparation for carrying out one of the component functions of the appointment—teaching. The present proposal is not that we eliminate the teaching assistantship but that we use it imaginatively to train college teachers.

Under the circumstances, it is not surprising that faculty members feel themselves ill prepared for teaching, and since their professional status is largely dependent on the judgments of their colleagues—

which in turn are based on scholarly works—it is natural that they find the laboratory or the library more congenial environments than the classroom. Hence, they gladly hand over the latter to the teaching assistant, with the reassuring suggestion, "If you have any problems, feel free to drop by my office any time." After that, they may briefly visit the TA's class once or twice, but in an evaluative more than a helpful role. In the meantime, the teaching assistant is a *de facto* college teacher—not a future college teacher. The institution, the department, and the individual faculty supervisor all share a double responsibility—to the undergraduates on the university campus and to the undergraduates whom the graduate student will teach when he completes his degree and goes elsewhere. There is no other source for college teachers. To me, this argues for a program of help and guidance that will contribute to meeting both responsibilities. Such a program need not be either long or massive—indeed, one of its characteristics should be maximum efficiency. But this is not likely to be achieved without careful planning, consistent effort, and the systematic monitoring of results.

THE COMPLEAT COLLEGE TEACHER

That *some* kind of preparation for teaching is helpful there can be little doubt. But what kind? I suggest you make a fundamental error when your first response to this question is to ask for some models that have been developed by other institutions or departments, with the idea of simply borrowing one that seems to make sense. I suggest instead an approach that first asks the question: What are the roles and functions for which you are training your graduate student-teachers? Having determined these, the particular program that is established should then be a function of your answers and of the nature of the institution, the faculty, and the students. It is possible to categorize the activities and competencies of college teachers under six headings. These "dimensions of college teaching" are: (1) content mastery; (2) the ability to organize a domain of knowledge, to design and plan a course, to establish instructional objectives; (3) effective presentation skills—the "management of learning"; (4) personal interaction with students both inside the classroom and out; (5) ability to rigorously evaluate one's own teaching effectiveness; and (6) professionalism. Assuming the utility of some such classification scheme, it follows that any program designed to train college teachers must take into account each of these dimensions of the role. First a decision should be made about the kinds of skills and knowledge—and the amount of each—that is considered desirable, and then a program can be designed to these specifications. Following are some thoughts about each of the six dimensions.

Content Mastery

It is generally held that one must know something in order to teach it, and that the teacher's information should be up to date. In many cases, first-year graduate students receive TA appointments, but they do not always possess the content knowledge that is desired. In a viable training program, there should be some procedure for determining the graduate student's content mastery and remedial measures should be provided where necessary. An excellent method for achieving these ends is a series of weekly "prep" sessions in which the graduate student performs the current experiment, is presented with the most common undergraduate questions and sources of misunderstanding, and participates in the formulation of effective explanatory tactics and devices. This implies, of course, a reliable source of information on undergraduate needs relative to the principles under study. This scheme allows the new TA to discover for himself his content gaps and errors with minimal threat to his self-image. It should be further observed that if the teaching task is found rewarding by the new TA (and this depends largely on the departmental Zeitgeist), it can contribute significantly to his own learning. This is an implementation of the old saw, "The way to learn something is to teach it," the truth of which can be attested by almost any teacher.

Course Design

Another set of tasks in which college teachers are expected to exhibit some competence are those related to the organization of a domain of knowledge—choosing topics and sequencing them to make a coherent whole, choosing reading lists, deciding on appropriate ways to evaluate the academic performance of students, and establishing instructional objectives. I would argue that the last-named component is really the most important, because if the teacher can clarify for himself what he expects the students to accomplish, he will have provided himself—and his students—with a conceptual basis for making all the other decisions. This is a step that is too often overlooked, mostly because college teachers usually lack a systematic framework for thinking about the problem, central though it is. What follows is a brief discussion of just such a framework.

In the first place, instructional objectives always have two aspects: content and performance. Content is familiar to all instructors—it is conventionally shown in the course syllabus as a sequence of topics.

Meiosis and genetic theory are two examples on quite different levels. What is often overlooked is that every statement of a content objective implies some kind of intellectual performance. I suggest that there are five different kinds of performance, any one of which can be sought in connection with a given topic.

1. Students can be asked to simply *recall* the information. They can be asked, for example, for the verbal definition of meiosis. It must not be thought that this level of performance can be ignored; one must "have" a piece of information before he can put it to use. A skilled teacher will want to know whether his students' difficulties are due to an inability to apply information or whether they simply don't know it, because this information will have clear implications for his teaching methods.

2. Students can be asked to *apply* principles or rules to new material or situations. If they understand meiosis at this level, they can predict the outcome of the process, given an organism which they have never before seen. It is appropriate to consider "mastery of the investigative skills of the discipline" in this category. By this I mean the way one goes about doing scholarly work—the kinds of phenomena that are studied, the kinds of equipment that are used, the set of operations one follows in answering questions, and what constitutes evidence for or against a proposition. These things vary with each discipline. They amount to thinking in terms of professionals in the discipline.

3. Students can be asked to *analyze* a complex array or occurrence and identify specific entities or patterns that are instances of the abstractions of the discipline. For example, they can be expected to tell the difference between meiosis and some other process which is similar to it; they can find an abductor muscle in the frog when asked to do so, and so on.

4. Students can be asked to perform inductive operations, such as *interpreting or summarizing* a body of evidence. Here they must formulate for themselves generalizations that will adequately represent the data available. To remain with our familiar illustration, this could amount to asking the student to derive the principles of meiosis from having seen many examples of the process in different organisms.

5. Students can be asked to *draw new implications,* to extrapolate beyond what is known, to create new products. This is a creative activity, probably most often seen in designing a new experiment to test a question.

There are many other ways to classify intellectual operations, but this is a serviceable set. The main point is that the student can be asked to deal with the same principle or bit of information in quite different ways, and the teacher should be aware of what he is asking, because, again, this decision has implications for his teaching and his evaluation methods. A teacher should not delude himself that he is training students to apply information when his tests call for little more than an accurate memory of what was said in lecture.

It should be pointed out that some of the most important objectives that college teachers have are, in a sense, "noncontent" in that they are attitudinal in nature. Such things as "exciting the curiosity of the student" or "greater sensitivity to our natural environment" would be included here. I would argue that these are quite legitimate objectives—the fact that grades might not be assigned on the basis of relative achievement of these objectives does not invalidate them. Indeed, they may be the very essence of what is called a "liberal education."

The components of course design discussed above are far from being trivial tasks. It is one thing to perform well in graduate courses when the structure of the content has been given you; it is quite a different matter to structure it for oneself. And some skill in course design is expected of a college teacher. For these reasons, some work in this area should be a part of any training program. A device that serves this purpose very well calls for each graduate student, at about the time he is working on his dissertation, to write up a complete proposal for an undergraduate course in his special area of expertise. After review and advice by an appropriate committee, the course should then be offered and conducted by the student; the experience and the results should be recorded in his departmental folder.

MANAGEMENT OF LEARNING SKILLS

I submit that the phrase "management of learning" is a felicitous one, inasmuch as it is a broader concept than something like "teaching technique," which tends to be identified with in-the-classroom activities. The skillful college teacher realizes that only part (perhaps only a small part) of the students' learning takes place in the classroom. It is up to the teacher to direct the students' learning through effective use of the total resources of the institution or even the surrounding community. This is done through wisely chosen and assigned outside activities that complement the abstractions dealt with in the classroom. Another device whose *teaching* potential is seldom realized is the examination, or paper, or project, or other evaluation instrument. Still other opportunities lie in the imaginative use of various automated devices such as prerecorded audio or 8 mm movie cassettes, or the increasingly available computer terminal. One expects the skillful college teacher to choose among these devices or to use the "standard" instructional techniques of lecture, discussion, demonstration, etc., in the service of predetermined instructional objectives. It is not the case that all methods of instruction are equivalent; students learn best what they practice. Therefore the teaching method employed should give them practice in the kinds of activities that are representative of the chosen objectives.

It should be clear from the foregoing that a mark of the skillful teacher is the range and flexibility of his repertoire. This realization has implications, in turn, for the training program. If TAs only conduct discussions or recitations or labs, their experience is severely circumscribed and inadequate. TAs need practice in doing all the kinds of things that college teachers in their discipline do. There is no excuse for denying them the opportunity to organize and present lectures, if, as a professional, they will be expected to lecture. The objection that they are not knowledgeable enough amounts to little more than obfuscation and subterfuge. When a student reaches the dissertation stage of his career, he must know enough about *something* to be listened to with respect.

PERSONAL CONTACT WITH STUDENTS

For a teacher to be effective at most educational levels, it is necessary to have some feeling for the students—to understand their views of what is going on, to respond to their needs, to respect them. I am not suggesting that teaching assistants try to make every class session into a group therapy period, but the fact is that each of us comes through as a human being every time we contact another person. We communicate ourselves at every moment, whether we will it so or not. Indeed, it is quite impossible to *not* communicate. In this personal contact with students, both inside the classroom and out, four characteristics are paramount. They are, first, accessability, which means real, personal, physical availability to the student—not simply a meaningless invitation to "drop in the office sometime." The second quality is authenticity—an honest presentation by the teacher of how he sees himself as a human being—his values, goals, attitudes, and convictions, and his reasons for having them, stated as honestly as he can manage them. The third characteristic is the possession of useful knowledge, such as information about specific teachers with whom a given student will feel most congenial or simple ways to register for the next semester. And the last quality is the ability to relate to students. Probably the two most important components of this last quality are a capacity for really listening—carefully, fully, and with as few preconceived ideas as possible, and an awareness of your own feelings. These are very easy things to identify in the abstract, but some of them are extremely difficult to do. It is inappropriate for a training program to try to make trained counsellors of each TA, but we all have our individual, personal strengths and weaknesses and our habitual ways of behaving. With a little reflection, it is easy to see that these, in turn, have fairly consistent effects on other people. It is in the best interests of any new college teacher to know what these are—because only then can he bring his personal contacts under control—for the benefit of his students. Almost every TA can use some help in this regard; every training program should have it available.

Self-evaluation

The skillful college teacher is one who can objectively evaluate his own effectiveness. The most familiar pattern of evaluation of TAs is a class visit or two by a faculty member. Such visits tend to be rather more inhibitory than helpful, and they are based on the assumption that the visiting faculty member can adequately judge, within the small space of time allotted, the complex enterprise called teaching. I hope that this paper will cast this assumption in doubt. But even if such devices were successful in identifying the true strengths and weaknesses of the new teacher, they contribute very little to his capacity for accurate *self*-evaluation. This can be developed if the TA learns a process that can be called "teaching-by-objective."

Just as the objectives of a training program must be more explicitly formulated "to produce good college teachers," so it is necessary for the individual teacher to have clearly fixed in his mind what he is trying to accomplish when he undertakes to teach a course. As part of a training program, the TA's instructional objectives can be reviewed for their appropriateness to the discipline, the character of the institution and the department, and the level of the students. The best, indeed the only, criterion for these decisions is the considered judgment of scholars in the discipline. The *effective* teacher can then be defined as one who sets up objectives and attains them. The *good* teacher is the effective teacher who attains the "right" objectives, i.e., those that are congruent with the highest scholarly judgments of desirability and appropriatenesses.

There are four components to evaluating one's own teaching efforts: (1) A formal *written* statement of objectives. Memories are unreliable things, and it is easy to forget by the end of the semester just what it was one set out to do 4 months previously. An objective record is a self-commitment. (2) The design and implementation of teaching methods and strategies that are calculated to attain the objectives.

(3) A determination (at the time the objectives are formulated) of the kinds of evidence that are necessary to allow judgments about one's success in reaching the objectives. This is followed by actual collection of these kinds of evidence. (4) Comparison of the result obtained in (3) with the objectives stated in (1). This is followed by interpretation and revision of objectives, teaching methods, and/or evaluation procedures. The cycle is repeated for each teaching task. It is suggested that once a certain degree of skill is acquired in the appropriate terms in which to state objectives and in developing valid evaluation measures, the individual teacher has a built-in self-correcting system that will go a long way toward enabling him to dispassionately evaluate his own teaching effectiveness. The individual's increasing effectiveness as a teacher can be defined in terms of the degree to which his students' achievement approaches his present goals and/or the degree to which his goals increase in sophistication.

Whether or not a scheme such as the one outlined above is incorporated into a training program, the point that some device for teaching the TA how he can go about objectively evaluating his own progress as a teacher is one that should be dealt with. Simply collecting student evaluations of courses is not the answer, because with a little experience, most teachers begin to realize that some of the educational goals which they espouse for many reasons are often misunderstood or considered irrelevant by students.

PROFESSIONALISM

Under this heading I consider a number of things. In general, they differentiate the scholar from the instructor. The former is one who conceptualizes the teaching task in terms of the overall education of the student and the welfare of society, as well as his personal needs, aspirations, and limitations. Other qualities are productivity in administrative assignments, skill in counselling students, the guidance of less experienced teachers, knowledge of institutional practices in respect to hiring, promotion, public service, etc., familiarity with the structures and functions of professional organizations in the discipline, knowledge of the variety of curricula that presently exist in his discipline with some understanding of the rationale for each, and a reasonably well developed personal philosophy of education.

I submit that one's personal educational philosophy should be made explicit, because only then can it be examined. It is a fairly straightforward task. A series of questions such as How much influence should students have over course content?, To what people or institutions do you have responsibilities as a college teacher?, and Should grading standards be absolute or curved—or should there be grades at all? when asked of a group is guaranteed to promote extended discussion. With a little guidance, each participant can be shown to have a set of values that together constitute his working educational philosophy. The group discussion process will also make him rethink some components. A serious training program for college teachers will provide opportunities for TAs to acquire the various competencies identified in this section.

This completes my exposition of the dimensions of college teaching. If the discussion has been long, it is because the task is a complex, multi-faceted one. It is suggested that the design of a training program begins with decisions about the trainee's desired competence in each of the six areas. In the following section, I will discuss how one uses these specifications as the basis for designing a program.

DESIGNING A TRAINING PROGRAM

Given a series of decisions about the kinds and amounts of competence considered desirable for graduating doctoral students, there remains the task of creating devices and procedures that might reasonably be expected to achieve these ends as efficiently as possible. At this point, it would probably be helpful to select a specific, realistic goal of a training program in college teaching and engage in the design process itself. The goal I have selected might be stated: "The teacher will feel comfortable and self-confident in his teaching activities." It is common for people who are working with new TAs to state this as an important goal; I hope the reader does not consider it trivial. It certainly is not trivial to the beginner. But let us examine somewhat closely the goal as stated. I have made the point previously that the *raison d'etre* for a teacher is the education of his students— not his personal amusement or aggrandizement. The goal I have chosen is entirely consonant with that statement. A little reflection will tell us that the teacher who is anxious and unsure of himself and what he is doing is not likely to do much creative thinking on the instructional process. To the extent he gets stage-fright when he finds himself before a group of students, or panics at the thought that someone might (and probably will) ask a question for which he does not know a full scholarly answer, his energies are being used in the defense of his own self-image and sense of worth and are being diverted from the principal mission of a teacher. Therefore, it is reasonable to want our TA to feel comfortable in the classroom.

How to proceed? The first step is to decide what kind of evidence we will accept as indicating that a teacher is comfortable and self-confident. In short, we want to know what we are looking for or we run the risk of not recognizing it when (or if) it occurs. A few moments reflection will tell us that there are several signs that would be helpful. One would be the TA's flexibility—his refusal to be bound by a lesson plan or a set of notes. If his plan is not achieving the effect he wanted, he can change. Bear in mind that there are other factors involved in the ability to change teaching method in mid-class session, such as some readily available alternative ways of working toward the instructional goal. But self-confidence and an internal sense of comfort are certainly among them. Secondly, the TA does not exhibit nervous reactions—he does not sweat, his voice does not quaver, his color is normal. Thirdly, he is willing to engage in give and take with students—he does not brush off students' inquiries and comments because they seem to be straying away from his plans. He does not use sarcasm—ordinarily a sarcastic person is a threatened person. He does not attempt to exert his authority improperly or unnecessarily. He looks the students in the eye. He is accessible to students—he comes to the classroom a few minutes before the beginning of the class period, and he remains for individual conversations after the period is over. Furthermore, if a peer observes his class, and some sort of minor disaster occurs, he can discuss the matter afterward without getting unduly defensive. He can accept the fact that he, like any other teacher, sometimes blows an opportunity and that the most constructive response to such an occurrence is to learn from it. Where is this evidence to be gathered?—in the classroom, because that is where the directly relevant phenomena are.

Now that we know what kinds of signals we are looking for, we can ask: What kinds of mechanisms or procedures are likely to bring about the desired state of affairs? I will suggest four or five. But let me warn the reader that if he simply says to himself, upon seeing some particular device mentioned, "Yes, that should do it—I would do that," he is missing the point of this exercise. Each of the suggestions should be seen as an illustration and weighed against its other effects and how it fits in with other aspects of a program. Then the suggested devices will have served their purpose.

The first one that occurred to me was the use of microlectures, delivered to a group of other graduate students (or, preferably, undergraduates) and recorded on videotape. The TA can then view the tape in private or with a trusted colleague. The latter is preferable, because then he can see not only how he actually behaved, but how that behavior affects other people. A useful, but unconventional, way to make such tapes is to train the camera on the audience, where their reactions can be seen directly. The most sophisticated, but expensive, way to do the recording is through a split-screen technique which shows the teacher and audience at the same time.

A second device that might be considered is a series of presentations in some kind of seminar on college teaching. It is inappropriate to talk to the graduate student *about* presentation methods—he must actually do it, first in as unthreatening an environment as possible, followed by increasing assumption of the full instructor's role. If such a seminar were conducted like a workshop, in which a group of TAs practiced together, there is an excellent opportunity to build an atmosphere of trust among the TAs—making it easier and more likely that they will voluntarily consult with each other on teaching problems.

Sensitivity training is a third device which is often useful for helping people accept immediate feedback on the way they affect other people and use it productively. Often this response (from others) is negative, but the atmosphere in which it is offered (in the sensitivity group) robs it of much of its threat, and considerable insights into one's own behavior can often be gained in a relatively short time. Most university campuses have people skilled in sensitivity training techniques, and this can be a valuable resource for dealing with our problem.

Still a fourth way to contribute to the TA's comfort in the classroom is to help him better understand the principles and concepts of the course, so that he feels sure of his information when he addresses his class. Almost all graduate students respond well to this idea—they always feel more comfortable when they know what they are talking about. Earlier in the discussion of content mastery as a mark of the effective college teacher I mentioned a useful way to achieve this result. It is well to note in this connection that it is often the case that a given training device will contribute to several different dimensions of college teaching. In discussing the next suggested device, I will go into some detail on this important point.

A fifth device for improving the TA's comfort in the classroom is the simple one of having him sit in and observe classes taught by another person, preferably an experienced TA. There are two situations in which the observation of other teachers is particularly useful: one in which the observer is already in command of the content—enabling him to give his complete attention to classroom dynamics; the second is to observe a class in a discipline about which he knows absolutely nothing. In the presence of esoteric jargon that prevents him from understanding what is going on, the observer is again freed to study the teaching-learning process directly. By seeing how other teachers react to the kinds of situations that arise in any classroom, he gets useful clues on modes of coping. And this kind of knowledge helps him to feel better prepared, and hence more comfortable, especially if the observations take place before he is required to confront the situations himself. Brief, informal conversations with the teacher who was observed will reinforce these effects.

How does one choose among the five training devices mentioned above? One important criterion is the number of *different* contributions that are made by the one procedure. In order to discover what these are, it is necessary to analyze, in a rational and straightforward manner, the *set* of benefits that might be expected to accrue from its use. This requires no specialized skills—simple, logical reflection is all that is needed. Let us do such an analysis for the last device mentioned—observation of classes taught by experienced teachers. One benefit has already been identified—a knowledge of some ways of dealing with everyday teaching problems and students' response to these coping methods. This would be considered a component of management-of-learning skills—one of the categories of teacher competence discussed earlier. At the same time, the neophyte can be learning other components in the same category, such as a knowledge of a range of teaching techniques and the effects they have on students. In addition, he can begin to see the factors that conrtibute to "good" and "bad" classes. But observation can also contribute to knowledge along other dimensions. For example, by closely following the course of development of a lecture or a discussion, he is able to see the qualities of organization brought to the material by the teacher—part of our teacher dimension called "course design" earlier. Furthermore, to the extent that the observer's content knowledge was clarified by events in the class, this constitutes a contribution to the dimension "content mastery." And finally, the observer has an excellent chance to see the effect on students of a particular instructor's personality— their response to his characteristic behavior patterns. This is a contribution to our category "personal contact with students." A similar analysis can be carried out for any training device. The point is that no device is unidimensional in its effect. The choice of a specific one is properly based on the anticipation that all, or most, of its effects are desired and are not adequately represented elsewhere in the program.

To recapitulate: we now have a conceptual framework for developing a set of goals for a training program, a procedure for determining the kinds of evidence we need for making judgments of success or failure, and a way of choosing training devices. The last component is the collection of the relevant data, in whatever detail and completeness is deemed necessary, and a comparison of the obtained results with the previously specified goals. Frequently, this leads to revisions of goals, devices, or kinds of evidence collected, and a new cycle begins.

In this sense, the scheme is self-correcting. Lest the importance of this last component is underrated as a result of the brevity of its description, it is proper to point out that the entire system will fail to function unless this phase is implemented. It is a difficult task to formulate a set of goals for a training program, and the formulation becomes little more than an intellectual exercise unless a serious attempt is made to evaluate the attainment of the goals and to use such evaluation as a step toward further improvement.

We are now at the point where we can reconsider the utility of asking what training schemes or devices are being used by other departments or institutions. *If* we have determined our needs (goals) beforehand, and if a rational analysis of a given training device indicates that it will meet our needs, it is appropriate to consider its adoption. In the absence of such preliminary steps, we run the risk of a treadmill of intuitive judgments, based on unspecified assumptions, and evaluated by unknown criteria—a condition with a long history, but one hardly distinguished by outstanding success.

THE MICHIGAN PROGRAM

The Michigan College Teacher Training Program is a research and development project involving five departments (Botany, History, Philosophy, Physics, and Psychology) and the University's Center for Research on Learning and Teaching.

The overall program has three basic objectives. First in the evolution of a coordinated multi-departmental plan for training college instructors; second is the elevation of the status and image of the graduate student teaching assistants to a level which is consistent with the maturity and professional responsibility that are properly associated with the role of college teacher; third is the development of reliable and objective procedures and instruments for evaluating the effectiveness of teaching activities and of the training program and its components. Most of the training activities per se are carried out in the departments; Center personnel serve as consultants and as a communication channel between departments, while concentrating most of their attention on the problems of evaluation of the program and on the development of a conceptual model that specifies the qualities of an effective training program, regardless of the particular training devices or administrative arrangements involved.

The typical structure of the program within a given department includes a faculty Coordinator, a small group of Level III senior or supervising teaching assistants (hereinafter, "Instructors"), a larger group of Level II "Teaching Fellows," whose students are paid from University funds and who are typically autonomous teachers of undergraduate classes, and a relatively large number of Level I "Trainees"—beginners who are teaching for the first time. From two to four Trainees are assigned to each Instructor, who serves as mentor and guide.

Most formal training activities are directed toward the Trainee, since he customarily has had little or no teaching experience. The most common training devices include: First, actual classroom teaching, most of it under the direct observation of an Instructor, the amount ranging from 1 or 2 hours in Psychology to an entire term as a recitation leader in Botany or a laboratory assistant in Physics. Second, there is much discussion between Instructor and Trainee during the planning period which precedes teaching, with the latter serving in a guiding, helping—rather than a directing—capacity. There are also meetings and feedback conferences between Instructor and Trainee after the latter's teaching. Third, there are weekly discussion meetings of Trainees, Instructors, and Coordinators, dealing both with content and with teaching problems. The fourth common device is joint participation by Trainees and Instructors in the development and grading of examinations.

There is a heavy reliance in the program on Instructors since it is probable that another graduate student who is an experienced teacher is likely to be a much more available, approachable, and helpful teaching advisor than most regular faculty members; advanced graduate students who volunteer for the Instructor position are likely to be deeply committed to teaching; and the necessity for providing guidance and advice to a neophyte facilitates the evolution in oneself of a carefully thought-out personal philosophy of education. The Instructor's role itself was designed as a learning experience, and it is found to be so by its occupants.

Each department is exploring variations on the basic plan outlined above. In the Botany department, teaching assistants oversee the laboratory and conduct recitation sections. The department conducts a 1½ day "pre-session" before the opening of the Fall term, covering topics such as departmental structure and resources, the conceptual framework of the course (which features an audio-tutorial laboratory), techniques of teaching, lesson planning, and the use of equipment. In addition, there are weekly 3-hour "prep" sessions throughout the term, in which teaching assistants who are unfamiliar with the topic or experiment scheduled for the following week perform the experiment, and there is discussion and explication of the kinds of problems undergraduates customarily encounter.

To better prepare Instructors for their role as mentors to beginners, the Center conducts a 2-day interdepartmental workshop early in the Fall term. Most of the presentations are made by experienced Instructors in the various departments, with one day being devoted to the consideration of teaching methods and strategies and the other to the kinds of problems encountered by and with Trainees. The format alternates formal presentations with "application sessions" and deals with such topics as the psychology of learning, the structuring of teaching and training activities in the service of previously chosen objectives, the identification of some common problems faced by beginners, and useful ways of dealing with them. The workshop has three basic objectives. First, an understanding by the Instructors of the commonality of teaching-learning processed across disciplines (to facilitate their learning from each other) ; second, the willingness and ability to conceptualize and implement instructional activities in terms of a priori goals (to help them rationally direct their own efforts) ; and third, a knowledge of common issues that arise in guiding Trainees, along with suggestions for dealing with them (to contribute directly to the Instructors' effectiveness as mentors).

Some moves that have been taken in the various departments to increase the status of the TA include: (1) trainees are paid at regular TA rates, even though they sometimes do not carry the full responsibilities of the position; (2) systematic guidance and remedial help are consistently available to beginning teachers; (3) the work of faculty Coordinators is officially recognized as a staff function in the departments, comparable to service on an administrative committee; (4) virtually all incoming graduate students are enrolled as Trainees, in a move to make some training in teaching an integral part of the Ph.D. program; (5) performance as a Trainee is becoming a significant factor in subsequent departmental awards of regular teaching assistantships; and (6) TAs serve as regular members of departmental committees. To determine the degree to which these moves have succeeded in raising the status and prestige of the TA, Center personnel are conducting a survey among representative faculty members and graduate students.

The search for the solution of evaluation problems has been pursued most consistently by Center personnel. It has taken two forms. The first involves demonstrating to Instructors and Trainees the utility of first formulating instructional goals followed by the design of teaching methods calculated to attain them and supplying practice in the procedure. The second entails the cooperation of department and Center personnel in stating some goals of specific training devices and the collection of appropriate evidence to determine the degree to which the devices are successful. In addition, the Center conducts an annual mail survey of Ph.D. graduates of the departments one year after they have accepted academic appointments elsewhere to determine their opinion of the adequacy of their preparation for college teaching and to request their suggestions for improvement. This information is fed back to the departments as a guide to future development of the training programs. This completes a review of the Michigan program as it has evolved over a period of 3 years.

THE IDEAL PROGRAM

QUALITIES OF AN IDEAL PROGRAM

In this section, I will suggest the criterial qualities of the ideal training program and some classes of mechanisms that are calculated to attain these qualities. Then I will offer two variations of a specific proposal which could be expected to meet these criteria.

On the basis of our experience to date, it is becoming clear that meaningful impact on the academic community relative to the improvement of teaching and the training of new college teachers will be piecemeal and uneven so long as we expect all training of graduate students, in teaching as well as in their content area, to be dependent upon, controlled by, and implemented through the individual departments. The instructional agency, from the standpoint of the undergraduate student, is not the department but the institution. It is therefore appropriate to look for vigorous leadership in training in teaching at the university level. These statements should not be taken to urge the absolution of the departments from all responsibility in the matter—the argument is that the institution has a duty that overarches those of the departments and is complementary to them. But so long as there is not a consistent and forceful university policy, there is no alternative but to look to the various disciplines for appropriate action. In the discussion that follows, the criteria and most of the suggestions for implementation are equally applicable on both levels. What is being urged is that departments begin meeting their own responsibilities more fully than has been the case, while lobbying vigorously for proper institutional support.

It is proposed that the ideal training program has seven criterial attributes. In the first place, it is *complete*, in the sense that appropriate mechanisms exist for the adequate development of graduate students along each of the six dimensions of college teaching. This assumes that the overall objective of the program is to prepare college teachers. If that is not the case, if the TAs are seen as overseers of laboratories and graders of papers, obviously such a system as the one suggested here is unnecessary. On the other hand, it should be admitted that the TAs are being employed as academic handymen, not being trained as apprentice professionals. Of course, it is understood that a program can be considered complete only under two conditions: there is appropriate training in all the dimensions; and it can be shown that the training is successful. This requires adequate evaluation—meaning an objective procedure that is as independent as possible of the personal ego-involvements of the designers and participants.

Secondly, the program should be *efficient,* in the sense that redundancies among training devices should be avoided unless there is an indication that more than one kind of input is necessary to accomplish a desired end. It will be impossible, of course, to determine the degree of efficiency attained unless there is some method for evaluating outcomes. This, in turn, entails the process of stating objectives, designing and implementing training experiences, and collecting appropriate evidence. Since most content-oriented scholars have little talent or desire for engaging in some of the knottier aspects of evaluation, some university-wide agency, staffed by people possessing the requisite skills, is needed. Without proper evaluation procedures, there is little hope of systematic progress.

Thirdly, the ideal training program must be *practical.* This means that the developing teachers must be given full opportunity to come to grips with real teaching, administrative, and counselling problems—with help and guidance of the kinds discussed earlier readily available to them. Formal courses *about* teaching, without a chance to apply the concepts studied, do not qualify on this score. Activities and information for which there is no clear use should be eliminated. There are some fairly subtle distinctions that should be made in this connection. Skills or information which appear to be of little use at one point in a person's development as a teacher may be highly desirable at another. For example, some of the competencies discussed under the teacher dimension called "professionalism" may be properly reserved for the later part of training—they would probably be seen as having little practical value in the beginning. These considerations have implications for the sequence of training experiences provided.

Fourth, a training program, if it is to be viable and productive, must be seen as *legitimate* by the academic community, that is, the devotion to scholarship and research that exists on virtually every campus must be broadened so that the teaching enterprise is accepted as worthwhile and is professionally rewarding. It is in respect to this quality that the active participation of the institution is probably most appropriate.

The respect accorded a faculty member by his colleagues in his content area is heavily dependent upon their judgments of his scholarship; his teaching effectiveness receives only scant attention. This is the Zeitgeist in which the TA operates, and he naturally emulates his role models. Programs devoted to training in teaching are not likely to be very successful until they become respectable. Some specific measures that can be taken within the department to increase the prestige and status of the teaching assistantship were mentioned in the description of the Michigan program, though that was not an exhaustive list by any means.

A fifth characteristic which a training program must have if it is to be maximally effective is *continuity,* by which is meant that, despite changing generations of graduate students and the shifting administrative assignments of faculty members, the information gained over a period of time must be cumulative and transferable. It is typically the case that as each new faculty advisor to TAs assumes the duties of his post, he tends to rely heavily on his personal opinion of the kind of training that is most useful and to set up a system which reflects his values. This mode of operation implicity assumes that there is relatively little to be learned from what has gone before—that one approach to training (as to teaching) is as good as another. And indeed this may well be true so long as there is no systematic analysis of the task, no rational choice of methods in the service of that analysis, and only informal, intuitive evaluation. It is interesting to note in passing that these three qualities are highly uncharacteristic of a man's scholarly work, but they are typical in the domain of teaching.

On the other hand, it is possible to work from an entirely different model. Decisions could be made, at the university or department level, about the kinds and degrees of college teacher competencies that are considered desirable (and attainable). These would then constitute criteria of success. It should be abundantly clear from our preceding discussion that there are a large number of alternative approaches to a given goal. Each faculty member who serves as advisor to TAs could then engage in a continuing quest for the most effective and efficient training schemes, and he could do this as a member of a group which extends across departmental boundaries and across time. Under the typical conditions that exist today, this is impossible. It is clear that the scheme proposed here requires two components. The first is a set of records that contain decisions about training objectives, mechanisms and procedures that have been tested, and the results obtained. These records need not be extensive, but they must be systematic to be useful. The second component is administrative in nature. There must be some continuing structure or agency, at either the university or department level, which is charged with monitoring the college teacher training activities of the unit. This can be a small office attached to that of the vice-president for academic affairs, on the university level, or a standing "teacher training committee," on the department level.

A useful training program must be *flexible*. If there is an overall university program, it must be possible for each college or department to introduce such variations as are necessary to meet its unique conditions. And within a departmental program, it must be possible to provide each individual with the help he needs. This implies diagnostic capacities and available resources. In this connection, it is particularly useful to differentiate between those graduate students who are strongly oriented toward a career in college teaching and those who intend to be primarily scholars. The former require a much broader range of training experiences than do the latter. While it is proposed that every graduate student would have some familiarity with the teaching task, if only as a lab assistant, grader, or tutor, it is clearly a waste of time and money for an individual with little talent for, or interest in, teaching to go through a complete training program.

Lastly, a teacher training program should be *progressive*. By this is meant that as the TA increases in skill and dedication to teaching, he be accorded steadily increased responsibility and autonomy, so that by the time he completes his degree he has some familiarity with all the roles of the college teacher, as they were analyzed in the first section of this paper. Keeping a TA in a structured position where his duties are clearly prescribed for him and where the tasks have been highly overlearned for more than a few months (or perhaps, weeks) cannot be defended as training. It is acknowledged that there are many relatively dull repetitive aspects to teaching and these must be accepted, but this is not all there is to teaching. If we do not take advantage of the problem-solving capacities, the motivation to teach, and the creativity of our graduate students by involving them progressively in the full range of activities associated with the role of college teacher, we are not meeting our responsibilities as trainers of new teachers. It is suggested that "TA" be taken to represent "Teaching Apprentice" rather than "Teaching Assistant."

A Proposed Program

The foregoing discussion of the characteristics of training programs may have created the impression that extensive and prolonged training experience is being suggested. This is not the case—it is doubtful that more than one year of (part-time) work can be defended as training. This is not to say that anyone can become a finished teacher in that time, but given a coherent and rationally designed program that meets the seven criteria presented above, a thorough acquaintance with all the six dimensions of teaching can be accomplished—an individual's development beyond that point must be a function of his own motivation and the opportunities of his professional position.

The following training program is designed to meet all the criteria proposed in the preceding discussion. The office of the vice-president for academic affairs of the university would initiate the program by offering the various academic units summer support for graduate students in exchange for systematic training and supervision in teaching during the academic year. Some reasonable formula would be developed involving a ratio between the number of summer support positions and the number of students trained per unit. The office of the vice-president would call for proposals from the departments—proposals which would specify in some detail the amount and kind of training they would provide, and the summer support would be contingent upon the acceptability of the proposals. A set of criteria and a suggested outline of an adequate program would be supplied, with the understanding that only the former were prescriptive. The most important single condition for acceptance of a proposal would be the quality and objectivity of the evidence that would be submitted at the end of each year to demonstrate the success of the training. The insistence on this one feature will encourage the departments to plan their training programs in terms of their desired outcomes. Each department would be expected to design and largely implement its own program in conformity with the general guidelines established. Continuation of funding for each successive year would be contingent upon receipt of satisfactory evidence of progress in TA teaching.

It is expected that since, under ordinary circumstances, summer financial support for graduate students is in relatively short supply, most academic units would find such a proposition attractive since it could also make a significant contribution to shortening the interval between bachelor and doctoral degrees. The department would agree to reduce the teacher trainee's course load by about one course for one semester, during which the more intensive part of the training takes place. Roughly one-eighth of the student's time would be committed for one term of *training* in teaching. If he were concurrently serving as a teaching assistant, that appointment would be considered additional. Most of the training would be provided by and through the department, though the use of resources external to the department would be encouraged where they were appropriate. These could be supplied or arranged by an "office of instructional resources" operating under the aegis of the vice-president.

In addition, the university would provide a "pre-session" for all new TAs, of some 3 or 4 days' duration, just before the beginning of the Fall term. The general format would alternate formal presentations and workshop-like activities designed to provide opportunities for the application of relevant principles. Some topics that could beneficially be included are: counselling students, evaluation of academic achievement, practice teaching followed by critiques by graduate students from other disciplines, innovations in teaching, educational technology, and explorations of personal philosophies of higher education, to name a few. Some careful planning would provide a smooth articulation between the pre-session and the individual departmental programs.

A great deal of latitude could be encouraged in the programs mounted by the departments. So long as a department could make a reasonable case for the kinds of skills it is attempting to develop in its TAs and so long as it could show evidence that it is achieving those ends, the particular form of the program is of little moment. However, as I pointed out earlier, in the absence of institutional leadership in this matter, the responsibility remains, and there is no alternative to action by the departments. There is no essential reason why most of the seven desirable qualities of an institutionally supported program cannot be realized on the departmental level, although somewhat greater problems would probably be encountered in respect to the acceptance of the legitimacy of the effort by content-oriented scholars. In addition, there might well be considerable duplication of effort and some difficulty in carrying out some of the more complex evaluations.

SOME SPECIFIC PROCEDURES

Teaching Apprentices as Mentors to Others

This section deals with some mechanisms that are sometimes adopted as part of teacher training programs. The discussion will concentrate on analyses of the advantages and disadvantages of each, including problems of implementation and some suggestions for improvements.

At several points in this paper, mention has been made of the use of experienced teaching apprentices as guides and mentors for beginners. This is a system that has been explored with considerable success in the Michigan program. (They were called "Instructors" in the earlier description.) When these mentors have been appropriately selected and prepared, they have proved to be most useful to newcomers, as well as increasing their own teaching skills and deepening their understanding of the educational enterprise. In general, it is best if these individuals are self-selected for the position. This implies, of course, that the position is an attractive one and is perceived by the graduate students as contributory to their professional careers. This, in turn, means that students who anticipate a college teaching career and who are stable, moderately sociable individuals are often highly motivated and effective mentors. In addition to these qualities, they should be completely familiar with the content and teaching problems of the courses in which their advisees operate. Two factors that can contribute significantly to the mentor's effectiveness are: (1) accurate expectations of the kinds of problems he is likely to encounter in advising a peer with regard to the complexities of teaching, as well as some useful ideas on how to deal with the problems when they do arise; and (2) an ability to objectively and rigorously evaluate his own advising activities. It is helpful to the mentor to be clear about the expectations he has for his advisees, to recognize his own limitations, and to know the kinds of evidence that are required to allow unbiased and reliable judgments of success. A mechanism that has been shown to be of use in preparing the mentor for his task is a workshop, conducted either before the beginning of the Fall term or soon thereafter. Experienced mentors can serve as excellent sources of information about the problems of the position, and practice can be given in the subtle and complex task of stating objectives (which in this case are cast in terms of the skills of the beginner), how it is to be known whether the objectives are attained, and what specific measures are likely to be both practical and effective.

The role of advisor, helper, and guide is more congenial than that of supervisor to most graduate students, and the functions of the position can be well served under these conditions. A mentor can work effectively with from four to six beginners on a quarter-time appointment if the proper steps are taken to facilitate regular contact among them, and with the proper logistical support. Lower ratios may be desirable from time to time, principally as a means of providing more senior graduate students with the experience, a useful component in an individual's development as a college teacher. Typically, mentors have little official authority over their advisees, and this has worked surprisingly well. Lacking the prestige and power of a faculty position, the mentor must convince the beginner, on logical, ethical, and/or empirical grounds, of the utility of a course of action. In the process, he must examine his own convictions and his reasons for having them —a broadening, though sometimes unsettling, operation.

There are several steps that can be taken to make the mentor role attractive to an eligible graduate student. One is an increase in autonomy and responsibility in his activities; it should be made clear what results are expected of him, and he should have free rein to accomplish them. Second, at this point it is entirely appropriate to involve him in the design and planning of courses and in departmental administrative assignments, such as membership on standing committees. Third, his higher level of competence can be confirmed by a stipend that is significantly above that of regular TAs. Fourth, his professional status can be increased by the granting of a distinctive title, such as "Instructor," and a record of his performance as mentor can be placed in his departmental folder. These last may be particularly valuable in connection with later job applications.

VIDEOTAPES AND MICROLECTURES

There is an increasing use of videotapes and subsequent playback as a component in the training of teachers at all levels. Most TAs who can bring themselves to face the "Big Brother" eye of the camera consider the experience helpful—at least for one or two exposures. When asked for a more detailed characterization of the benefits of the procedure, the most common response is that it provides the teacher with irrefutable evidence of the way he conducts himself. Essentially, then, it serves as a feedback device. However, this is not the only use to which videotape can be put, as will be explained below. It is possible, of course, that the benefits are largely motivational—it is ego-boosting (though a bit frightening at times) to see a record of one's activities, rather like a mention in the newspaper. If this is the principal function of the videotape-playback sequence, then perhaps no further justification is necessary.

It is possible, however, to use the device in more sophisticated ways. Clarity about the purpose of videotaping brief presentations by TAs has implications both for how the taping is done and for the kind of evidence that is needed to judge whether it was successful. The investment of time and money that is involved in the acquisition and operation of the system makes the issue a real one. The focus of attention can be the behavior of the teacher, a decision that assumes a knowledge of the instructional value of certain kinds of activities. To acquire these skills, then, is the goal of the taping, and of the training. The camera will be aimed at the teacher, and the tape will be a record of what he does. On the other hand, attention could center on the students, with the goal being that of helping the teacher become more sensitive to the reactions of his audience. The latter would appear to be the more basic criterion, since it is relatively unenlightening to know what a teacher does in the absence of knowledge of what its effect is. Videotaping, then, is optimally done with a live audience, and a significant proportion of the tape should contain a record of the audience's responses to what the teacher is doing. Split-screen techniques are ideal for this purpose, but they are expensive. In the absence of a record of audience response, it is entirely possible for the new teacher to attend, during the playback, to nonsignificant and/or irrelevant personal mannerisms and to be unaware of subtler but more important aspects of teacher-student interactions. On this argument, it follows that a group of undergraduates makes the most useful and appropriate audience if the proper arrangements can be made.

It is worthy of note at this point that the presence of the TV camera and its related equipment and personnel can have from very slight to strongly deleterious effects on the atmosphere and conduct of the class, depending largely upon the attitude of the teacher. If he is comfortable and essentially manages to ignore the camera, the students are very likely to follow suit and there is a natural flow to the class. If, on the other hand, the teacher is on edge or subtly resentful of the "intrusion" into his class, the effect is likely to be so stilted and atypical as to be next to worthless as a sample of normal classroom activities.

It has not been clearly demonstrated that the video system is essential for proper feedback. Rather, the crucial element is more likely to be the reactions of other people. At any rate, because the question is a moot one, it is advisable to approach the use of videotape with an inquiring attitude. It is possible to explore the reactions of other human beings to one's teaching efforts in less technologically dependent ways. For example, an alternative method would be the institution of a "buddy" system among TAs, in which pairs of individuals would attend each other's classes as silent observers, and later provide informal comments on the events that transpired. At any rate, the basic nature of videotape should be borne in mind; it is essentially an objective record of previous events, and, as such, is more or less interchangeable with other record-systems that preserve the elements of critical interest to the users. The fact that the video record is in some sense more detailed and more complete than a written record, for example, can prove to be an advantage or a handicap, depending upon how it is used.

FORMAL COURSES ON COLLEGE TEACHING

Most content-oriented scholars, including graduate students, are highly critical of formal courses in higher education or teaching methods, finding them either too abstract and vague to have any practical utility or so detailed as to be boring. I do not wish to go into the merits of this argument—I simply report it. In the face of this massive resistance, it is unwise to institute a series of lectures on the "teaching of X" because they are likely to be unattended. There may be one exception to this generalization. Graduate students who are about to receive their degrees and who expect appointments to academic positions are often receptive to one or two sessions at which they can receive accurate information about such topics as institutional practices relative to hiring, promotion, and public service, the structures and functions of professional organizations in the discipline, the administrative structure and governance of colleges and universities, and the kinds of curricula that exist and the rationales upon which they are based. In addition, of course, a good many graduate students are willing to read succinct but informative papers on the above topics and on the psychology of learning, academic evaluation, the nature of the college student, and specific instructional techniques. For those with such an interest, I have appended a brief annotated bibliography. It is well to remember, however, that simply reading about a concept such as "behavior modification" is likely to prove unrewarding unless it is accompanied by systematic attempts to apply the principles in teaching. Until such information is put to use, it remains psychological jargon.

Despite what has been said above, it is possible to develop a formally structured course that will be found useful by TAs, if care is taken to build in two basic characteristics. First, brief presentations of general principles must be alternated with practice by the participants in the application of the principles. Second, the content topics which are dealt with should be only those for which the TAs have a perceived need. If a topic is one about which college teachers should have some information, but which TAs reject (perhaps for lack of perspective and understanding), they must first be shown its relevance to their teaching problems. The course then assumes the nature of a workshop, dealing with very practical matters, and can be well received. An example of the kind of course being referred to here is rather like that reported by Frank Costin ("A graduate course in the teaching of psychology: Description and evaluation," *Journal of Teacher Education,* Winter, 1968, Vol. XIX, No. 4, pp. 425–432). Some of the classes of activities that seem appropriate for such a workshop might be: the generation of educational innovations in the service of a priori objectives; the development of new, more valid methods of evaluating the outcomes of college courses; sensitivity training, where the individual can become more aware of his effect on other people and more able to use the feedback he receives from them; the clarification and exploration of personal philosophies of education and the implications such philosophies have for everyday teaching; course planning; and the development of specific skills, such as leading discussions or explaining and working problems clearly and fully.

CLASS VISITS BY FACULTY

The most common single form of "supervision" of TAs by faculty is the class visit, sometimes followed by a feedback conference. The utility of this time-honored device is doubtful on several counts. First, there is the assumption that practically all that one needs to know about a teacher is clearly visible in any given class session. I take issue with this. If the reader will refer to the six dimensions of college teaching that were discussed earlier in this paper, it will become evident that a class visit can adequately assess only a fraction of the competencies of the role. One would certainly not want to make a judgment of the overall content mastery of a TA from one or two class performances. It is possible to obtain only a miniscule sample of the teacher's ability to organize a domain of knowledge or design a course. A few moments reflection will surely make clear that "management of learning" skills include such things as the forms of exams and outside assignments, and the nature of the criteria the teacher uses to discriminate between average and excellent work—none of which are usually available to the casual classroom observer. It is next to impossible to determine, under these circumstances, what the teacher's standards are for assessing his own performance. It is highly unlikely that one can get any notion of the individual's "professional competencies," as the term was used earlier. Some idea *can* be obtained of the TA's ability to guide a discussion smoothly or to explain an obscure point, and the qualities of the interpersonal dynamics of the classroom are reasonably apparent to a sensitive observer. In sum, class visits simply do not supply the necessary information.

The second weakness of faculty visits is the implicit assumption that there is a finite set of characteristics that mark the "good teacher," and that the visiting scholar knows them and can recognize them. The average faculty member probably has an image of the "ideal teacher," which is patterned after some teacher he himself studied under at some point in his educational career. But this image is largely the result of his personal experiences and reflects in large measure the interaction between his own personality and values and the style of his own paradigmatic teacher—hardly a basis for valid generalization. The literature on the subject clearly indicates that there are no easily discernible qualities that all good teachers share. Related to this point is the fact that most faculty members have very little systematic information on teaching—what they know is almost entirely the product of their own characteristics and experience. It is true that if this collective wisdom (and I believe it *is* true wisdom) could be pooled and ordered in some rational way for the benefit of the beginner, the whole enterprise would be enriched. This almost never happens.

The third count against the faculty visit is the implicit threat that exists. It is unreasonable to expect a second-year graduate student to perform at his normal operational level in the critical presence of someone who holds a great deal of power over his future. What is seen is almost surely atypical; one is therefore ill-advised to give great weight to such information in making important decisions about an individual.

However, it is possible to use class visits very effectively in improving college instruction, if the emphasis is on making the visit-plus-conference sequence a learning experience for both the person observed and the observer. This almost (but not absolutely) requires roughly equal academic status for the two individuals. An older, more experienced TA who has taught the course and who can work effectively with beginning teachers is an ideal choice for this task. His orientation should be that of helping the new man, rather than supervising or evaluating him. He can be of real service and will at the same time enlarge his own repertoire of teaching styles. These remarks must not be taken to exclude all faculty from making class visits; if they can adopt the stance suggested in this paragraph, they too can benefit. It still must be remembered, of course, that class visits—no matter who makes them—can be only a part of an adequate training program. The challenge is to get the most mileage possible out of them.

THE EVALUATION OF TRAINING DEVICES

It seems inappropriate to conclude this paper without giving some explicit attention to the task of determining whether each of the training devices that constitute a given program are indeed producing the effects desired. In an earlier section of this paper (cf., Designing a Training Program), there was a detailed description of how one establishes the putative goals of a training device. Once this is done, it becomes a matter of collecting the relevant evidence. It will be recalled that the device under discussion was the observation of an experienced TA by a beginner, and there were six possible effects suggested. Among them was "knowledge of a range of teaching techniques and the effects they have on students." The kind of evidence required is fairly clear—it involves the ability of the observer to identify one or more teaching "tricks" with which he was previously unfamiliar, and his ability to cite specific student responses to them. To be sure the observer's knowledge does not prove it was gained through *this* device. On the other hand, if the observer lacks this knowledge, we can say with some certainty that the observation device is not having at least one of the effects that could be reasonably expected of it, and remedial measures could be taken. The same general procedure can be followed for any other training device. These remarks must not be taken to argue the need for extensive and detailed records. The goal of this illustration was to make clear how one can objectively evaluate the components of a training program. Once this technique has been mastered, a program can develop rationally and systematically to meet the specific needs and conditions of the academic unit.

A BRIEF ANNOTATED BIBLIOGRAPHY

Brown, James, and Thornton, James. 1963. *College Teaching.* McGraw-Hill Book Co., New York.

The first part of the book deals with some interesting general issues in a reasonable, straightforward way. Recommended are the chapters of The context of higher education, The college instructor, The college student, and The curriculum of higher education. The remainder of the book is devoted to specifics of the teaching task, but these are better presented in the McKeachie book below.

Craig, Robert C. 1966. *The Psychology of Learning in the Classroom.* Macmillan Co., New York (paperback).

A nontechnical treatment of three theoretical conceptualizations of learning and the implications of each for real classroom teaching. It is understandable and useful to those without backgrounds in psychology, who want to know something systematic about the psychology of learning and teaching.

Gronlund, Norman. 1968. *Constructing Achievement Tests.* Prentice-Hall, Englewood Cliffs, N.J. (paperback).

A succinct coverage of the essentials of conventional academic testing, dealing with all the standard test forms, their advantages and disadvantages and how to make most effective use of them. A good introduction to the subject.

McKeachie, W. J. 1969. *Teaching Tips.* D. C. Heath, Lexington, Mass. (paperback).

A practical, down-to-earth approach to most of the everyday problems of preparing for a course, choosing reading lists, designing class formats, the use of various teaching techniques, and even some administrative tips. In many cases, the recommendations are supported by data from empiricial studies. A kind of manual for beginning college teachers.

Morris, W. M. (Ed.) 1970. *Effective College Teaching*. American Association for Higher Education, Washington, D.C. (paperback).

A series of thoughtful essays about teaching strategies characteristic of various disciplinary areas, as well as an interesting and useful description of the typical administrative structure of institutions of higher learning. General information worth knowing by anyone headed for a college teaching career.

3. Alternatives to the Traditional Ph.D.

In their search for better ways to strengthen the teaching component of graduate education, some have turned their efforts to finding an alternative for the Ph.D. degree. It is very easy to see how pursuit of the traditional Ph.D. with an almost exclusive preoccupation with the discovery of new knowledge fails to prepare graduate students for a lifetime of teaching at the college level, but it is not as easy to develop an acceptable alternative.

This discussion will concentrate for the most part on preparations at the Ph.D. level, but it should not be forgotten that a very large number of people will be teaching without doctor's degrees. According to Dr. Ann M. Heiss,[1] only 25% of those who enter higher education faculties each year have the equivalent of a doctor's degree and only 51% of experienced college and university faculty members have the Ph.D.

At the doctoral level, the choice would seem to be: the Doctor of Arts, the Ed.D., and the Ph.D. including modifications of that degree. The Council of Graduate Schools in the United States in its March 1970 statement made this distinction among the programs leading to Ph.D.-level degrees:

> Doctor of Arts "will parallel other doctoral programs but will be oriented toward developing teaching competence in a broad subject matter area."
> Doctor of Philosophy "is designed to prepare a graduate student for a lifetime of creative activity and research, although it will often be in association with a career in teaching at a university or college."
> Doctor of Education "should mark a professionally-oriented program at the doctoral level in a field of education."

DOCTOR OF ARTS

The increasing pressures to improve the quality of teaching preparation have focused much attention on the Doctor of Arts degree as a possible solution. Dr. Robert H. Koenker,[2] Dean of the Graduate

---

[1] Heiss, Ann M. 1968. *Preparation of College and University Teachers.* This paper was prepared as a Chapter in the report of the U.S. Commissioner of Education Assessment on *The State of the Education Professions,* August, 1968.

[2] Koenker, Robert H. 1970. Status of the Doctor of Arts and sixth-year degree programs for preparing junior college and college teachers (mimeographed).

School of Ball State University, states that no graduate program has received such wide acceptance in such a short period of time. The degree has been endorsed by the Council of Graduate Schools in the United States, the American Association of State Colleges and Universities, and several other professional associations, according to Dr. Koenker.

Financial encouragement will surely make consideration of the Doctor of Arts degree attractive. The Carnegie Corporation of New York has awarded ten one-year grants of $100,000 each to institutions planning to develop Doctor of Arts programs. Fellowships for candidates for the degree are available under Title V (E) of the Higher Education Act.

One would think from the quantity of discussion of the Doctor of Arts degree that it was a very popular program. As a matter of fact, although many universities are considering the degree, few have adopted it at present. In March 1970, at the time of the publication of Koenker's study, only three institutions offered the Doctor of Arts degree and only the University of North Dakota offered the degree to biology students. But at that time, 68 universities were launching, developing, or considering the possibility of developing a Doctor of Arts degree program.

The Doctor of Arts degree is designed to differ from the Ph.D. in emphasis but not in quality. Again and again proponents of the degree insist that it must be a degree of unimpeachable quality and under no circumstance should it be undertaken by institutions without the physical and human resources adequate to establish a first-rate program. They insist that the degree not be given as some sort of consolation prize to the less competent graduate students or be offered by institutions not quite able to make it in the big time. E. Alden Dunham[3] of the Carnegie Corporation makes the cogent suggestion that the test of quality is whether the institutions offering the Doctor of Arts would be willing to hire holders of the degree for responsible positions.

The guidelines established by the American Association of State Colleges and Universities[4] spell out in detail the precautions necessary to prevent the erosion of the quality of the degree.

---

[3] Dunham, E. Alden. 1969. *Colleges of the Forgotten Americans,* McGraw-Hill Book Co., New York.

[4] A pamphlet, *The Doctor of Arts Degree,* prepared by the American Association of State Colleges and Universities, is available from the Association at One Dupont Circle, Washington, D. C. 20036. The Council of Graduate Schools in the United States, at One Dupont Circle, will also furnish a pamphlet entitled *The Doctor of Arts Degree.*

The Council of Graduate Schools in the United States has set forth a definitive description of the Doctor of Arts program:[4]

First, the formal course work in the Doctor of Arts program will deal preponderantly with the subject matter to be taught by the prospective teacher. Course selection will typically be broader within a particular discipline than for the Ph.D. and may also bridge several related disciplines. The individual courses in the Doctor of Arts program will be conducted at the same high level as Ph.D. courses and where the two programs exist side by side may well be the same courses in many instances. Foreign language or other research tool requirements will be truly functional. A comprehensive examination which is typically broader and less specialized than the usual Ph.D. comprehensive examination but not less demanding will be required upon the completion of formal course work.

Second, prospective college teachers will take an appropriate amount of formal course work and seminars in such areas as the psychology of learning, the history and sociology of higher education, and the responsibilities of faculty members within an institutional setting.

Third, as a parallel to the traditional research training for the Ph.D. degree, a structured teaching or other appropriate internship will be required. This normally will not be met by the usual teaching assistantships. The teaching internship will include progressive and responsible classroom experience in regular courses, preferably in more than one kind of course. The internship will normally be held for one year and it will be supervised, criticized, and evaluated by experienced faculty members and reinforced by relevant course work in teaching methods which are applicable to the student's particular discipline.

Fourth, the development of the capacity and habit of reading, understanding, and interpreting the results of new research and pedagogical developments appearing in the literature of the field will be encouraged.

Fifth, development of the student's ability to apply new, significant disciplinary research and teaching techniques for the benefit of college teaching is a significant part of the student's graduate education for the Doctor of Arts degree.

Sixth, independent investigation of an area in the subject matter field will lead to a suitable written thesis. Such an investigation might take the form of research on teaching problems and may make a contribution to the teaching of the subject matter. The evaluation and synthesis of materials that are potentially valuable in college teaching but have not yet been reviewed may also be acceptable.

One virtue in the great amount of discussion of the Doctor of Arts degree is that it has stimulated people to think of what changes they would like to make in programs for future college teachers if they had a chance. The program being developed at the University of Illinois is a good example. This proposed program has some innovative features such as one might hope for in a new program. Students with a master's degree in biology will participate in a series of four semester-long tutorial workshops each concerned with a major area of biological organization (population, molecular, etc.). A third year will be devoted to a teaching internship and to the completion of a research thesis begun in the previous years. Not only will the student engage in hard research, he will also prepare a research proposal as part of his education. The internship, after two full years of work beyond the master's degree, will be carried out at a cooperating college. Finally, the student will return to the university at intervals after receiving his degree for continuing education and intellectual refreshment—what in less elegant terms is called retreading. The program is still on the drawing board, but it is a good example of how the development of a new degree program can stimulate the imagination.

Many people, convinced of the merits of the Doctor of Arts degree, still are concerned about the acceptance of this degree in the academic marketplace. Trevor Colbourn, Dean of the Graduate School of the University of New Hampshire, presented this point of view clearly at the CUEBS New England Conference:

> I am going to say very flatly that at this point I still need to be educated and persuaded as to the merits of the Doctor of Arts as the answer to our needs. . . .
>
> My biggest reservation on the Doctor of Arts is frankly pragmatic. To a point (only to a point I shall concede) a doctorate holder is as good as the ability of his department to place him reasonably, and right now this is by no means an academic point. As you well know, in many disciplines there is a serious surplus of Ph.D.'s on the marketplace desperately scrambling for relatively few positions. . . .
>
> I think it a useful illustration to recount that another university, at the end of last year, was seriously considering a series of Doctor of Arts programs. To that end it conducted a very serious study of its own marketplace: the community college and junior colleges for whom it contended its Doctor of Arts holders would be primarily destined.
>
> The results were rather startling. They indicated that the community colleges and the junior colleges who were expected to be just lusting for Doctor of Art's candidates said in effect, "No thank you; we can get all the Ph.D.'s we want at this point. Ph.D.'s carry prestige and status and we need both."

I am not arguing that the responses are necessarily correct responses; I am contending that this response signified something. It signified that at the present time there is the assumption in many quarters that the Ph.D. is a prestigious degree even if it is not perhaps the one that incorporates the proper training. . . . There is also the assumption that the Doctor of Arts is not in the same category, that because it will not be and cannot be, the Doctor of Arts holder is going to find himself in a very difficult position. He is going to be foreclosed from many possible appointments. He is going to be operating in what is presently, at least, a rather fragile market-place.

I am raising questions about the acceptability, about the real market-place for the Doctor of Arts. I am not so much questioning the virtues that the program can incorporate. The matter of status is, rightly or wrongly, a relevant issue to the academic marketplace. It is there.

Dr. Frederick Reif, who was instrumental in establishing the Ph.D. at the University of California, Berkeley, has the same anxiety about the acceptance of new degrees generally. His statement at the CUEBS conference at Berkeley illustrates his concern:

To illustrate the problem, I would mention my experience at a conference much like this one. It was attended by representatives of quite a few four-year colleges and dealt with the problem of the preparation of college science teachers. The question that I posed in trenchant form to highlight the problems was "We talk about the preparation of college science teachers. We talk about the desirable qualities these people ought to have. They ought to be very knowledgeable about their science, with good perspective of the field, with teaching experience. They should be creative. They ought to have *all* of these qualifications. Some complain that the universities often do not produce candidates who have these marvelous qualities; let us imagine an ideal world and have a university with a special degree program which attracts gifted students who are very innovative and very creative, with very good knowledge of the field. They not only like to teach, but to develop new curricular materials, to be intellectually alive—all of these beautiful properties. Let us give them a special degree like Ph.D. in Science Education—would you hire them?"

The answer was, "probably not if they don't have a Ph.D. degree. What we really want is the Ph.D. degree." If this is the prevailing attitude, one has to ask oneself the question: "What is the relation of current stereotypes to reality?" If one is interested in effecting certain ends, one ought to look specifically at the ends one has in mind or one may be misled by the stereotypes.

The admonition by Dr. Alfred F. Borg of the National Science Foundation, acting as chairman of the working group at the CUEBS Ann Arbor conference, is worth repeating:

> We had some discussion yesterday about other types of degrees, what are sometimes called practitioners degrees, a Doctor of Arts and so on. I think this movement is strong; it is not going to be turned aside. The trick is to make sure that adequate quality is built into programs and that practitioners degrees do not become a dumping ground for disposal of the mediocre. I think it is a losing battle to simply try to fight off or disregard alternatives to the Ph.D.

This plea for quality was repeated at every single CUEBS conference.

Doctor of Philosophy

Many feel that it is better to reform the Ph.D. and make use of the options within that degree than to develop a new degree. They would retain the Ph.D. as the basic degree for college teachers but they would make the teaching experience, presently part of most Ph.D. programs, a truly educational experience, not merely a service to the university. Most would add a seminar or other component on teaching.

Virtually everyone attending the CUEBS conference insisted upon the research experience as a vital component of the preparation of future teachers, but a large number felt that the research related to the teaching of the subject could very well make the contribution claimed for strictly discipline-oriented research. They would be pleased to see the thesis for some Ph.D. candidates be creative activity related to the teaching of biology.

Dr. Trevor Colbourn, Dean of the Graduate School at the University of New Hampshire, is one who advocates retaining the Ph.D. as preparation for college teachers. His statement at the CUEBS New England conference states his position clearly:

> My own conclusion is that the virtues of the Doctor of Arts, which are real, can and should be incorporated into the Ph.D. I feel that this is by no means the irreconcilable proposition. More challenging and more perplexing at times is the necessary task of persuading graduate faculty that this is a desirable development.
>
> I think that those who contend the Ph.D. today is an irrelevant degree have too often a justification to their complaint. I would hope that it might be possible for graduate deans and graduate faculty to work closely together in the future and find ways to remedy that complaint, to reform the Ph.D. to make it a relevant degree. They must not be hung up so obsessively with the research

component but pay more heed to the crying need for professional preparation for the college career for which most holders of the doctorate seem to be destined.

I would still argue for research competence. But I don't think that it has to be quite as large in its final dimensions as presently is usually required. In many disciplines it is a fact that 80–90% of Ph.D. holders, once they get their degree, publish nothing except their own name occasionally. In other words, for many, the Ph.D. is a terminal educational experience, at least it seems that way from at least one vantage point. This being the case, why is it we spend such an extraordinary amount of time on the dissertation? Why is it that we do not at least apportion a part of that time to the area of educational preparation, and professional training, so that a Ph.D. holder will go into the world knowing what world he is going into, knowing why he is going into it, and prepared to meet students and understand them and respond to them and meet their needs more effectively?

Dr. Edward C. Moore, Chancellor of the Board of Education of the Commonwealth of Massachusetts and strong proponent of the Doctor of Arts degree, feels just as strongly that the Ph.D. cannot and should not be made to accommodate the needs of the future college teacher. At the same CUEBS New England conference, he declared that since the Ph.D. is a research degree, a person pursuing that degree should not be distracted from his research by service as a teaching assistant and other activities said to prepare him for teaching. He does not feel that the teaching assistant experience is properly called preparation, and he has doubts about the competence of teaching assistants for the teaching they are now doing.

His view is best summed up in this quotation:

> If the Ph.D. itself were modified to have a heavy emphasis on teaching, this would be just as unfair to those who are not going into teaching as the present neglect of the concerns of those who will teach.

He would like to see the Ph.D. used to prepare people in research and the Doctor of Arts used to prepare people to teach.

E. Alden Dunham, another persuasive exponent of the Doctor of Arts degree, says in his book *Colleges of the Forgotten Americans* that it is unrealistic and perhaps even unwise to expect that the Ph.D. will be modified to "incorporate a knowledge of and respect for undergraduate teaching" for fear of undermining the Ph.D. as a research degree. In his words:

> The academic revolution has brought with it much that is undesirable, but it has also made American scholarship second to none in

the world. . . . Our major universities are in many ways at the center of our national life, and the nation is increasingly dependent upon the work of men trained at the highest levels of the Ph.D. and postdoctoral programs. I suspect that in the future even fewer of the top Ph.D. recipients will spend much time with undergraduate teaching or with problems of their own institutions. . . . Research Ph.D. programs are an inappropriate and inefficient way to meet the faculty needs of the bulk of American institutions of higher education.

Dr. Charles Lester, of the U. S. Office of Education, thinks that it is not necessary to devise new modifications of the Ph.D. He says that he cannot think of a single modification not already in practice.

One of the efforts made to enlist the talent and creative efforts of faculty with unassailable research credentials in the development of a program attempting to prepare outstanding college teachers of science is SESAME (Search for Excellence in Science and Mathematics Education), the program initiated by Dr. Frederick Reif at the University of California, Berkeley. Graduate students admitted to the program already have a master's degree or equivalent in the particular scientific discipline, but more important, they are selected as being intellectually gifted and possessed of a pioneering spirit.

The student is expected to achieve the same degree of academic competence in his discipline as any Ph.D. candidate in that field. He must also achieve some acquaintance with modern educational developments and he must have some teaching experience. His Ph.D. thesis consists of some research or development project dealing with curricular innovation or with the exploitation of new educational techniques. The degree awarded in the SESAME program is the Ph.D. in Science (or mathematics) Education.

At the University of Iowa, two-thirds of the work for a Ph.D. in Science Education is in two areas of science and one-third is centered in education. The thesis may involve a field of science or an area of science education. At Ohio State University and University of Maryland, among others, a thesis related to teaching of science may be used as part of the requirements of the Ph.D. in Science Education, and at the University of West Virginia and several others, such a thesis may be applied to a Ph.D. in Biology.

DOCTOR OF EDUCATION

Several universities prepare college biology teachers under a program leading to a Doctor of Education degree. The one at Ball State University is designed in such a way as to make moot the argument between the advocates of straight content and those who are equally committed to method. In their program a student and his advisor are free to tailor the student's program to his needs. As stated in the report of the CUEBS Michigan conference, if a student is intent on going into teaching in a two-year college, his program can be designed to fit that particular need. If a student is likely to teach in a college or university where research is a large part of his regular obligation and he will divide his time between research and teaching, he can be guided into a program that includes a good deal of straight discipline-oriented research.

OTHER DEGREES

Many other degrees requiring less time than a Ph.D. are available to future college teachers. Three relatively unfamiliar degrees are described here; in addition, many will teach with a master's degree in one of its various forms. *The Specialist degree,* as described in the brochure published jointly in 1969 by the American Association of State Colleges and Universities and the National Conference on the Intermediate Degree,[5] requires a higher level of study than the master's degree, but less emphasis on research than a Doctor's degree. In addition to a thorough study of the field of specialty and cognate areas, the program includes a supervised internship. It is intended that the Specialist Degree program include abundant opportunity for participation in research. In fact, some sort of scholarly project in the field of specialization is required.

The *Candidate in Philosophy degree* is awarded at several universities to those who have completed all work for the Ph.D. except the dissertation and are deemed eligible to continue to the Ph.D. if they should choose.

This degree recognizes the achievement of those who have reached this stage of their education. The Candidate degree was authorized in 1966, and since then over 1,000 certificates recognizing candidates have been awarded at the University of Michigan alone.

The *Master of Philosophy degree* is awarded Yale students who have completed all of their work except the dissertation. At Yale they have an interesting provision that anyone who wishes to interrupt his progress to the doctor's degree at this time will be placed in an intern position at a cooperating college where he will be paid as an instructor. It he chooses to return to Yale after a year or two of internship, he is assured an opportunity to continue on a stipend.

---

[5] This pamphlet is available from the Association at One Dupont Circle, Washington, D. C. 20036.

CONCLUSIONS

When one considers the great diversity of institutions preparing future college teachers and the enormous diversity in the positions to be filled, there would seem to be plenty of room for a variety of approaches to the preparation of the college teacher.

Some will find the Doctor of Arts the appropriate degree; some will prefer the Doctor of Education; some will find a six-year degree program best suited to their needs. The Ph.D. will probably continue to be the standard by which others are measured. The Ph.D. program has enough scope to provide for the production of creative teacher-scholars, scholar-teachers, and scholars. Some should qualify for the degree by doing creative work strictly in the subject matter as narrowly defined, while others do truly creative work related to the teaching of the subject. The same standards of originality, scholarship, and creative endeavor should apply in both cases.

No matter what the name of the degree taken by the future college teacher, he should be required to demonstrate that he knows the field and knows it well. It is not enough that he know the narrow specialty of his dissertation; he must have some breadth of knowledge of the field of biology and related scholarship.

It is essential that he has engaged in some research or other inquiry-oriented activity so that he knows the true meaning of investigation and knows it from experience.

It is also essential that there be some serious attention to teaching, preferably by actual practice in a program consciously planned to develop the teaching competence of the graduate student. His experiences as a teacher should be illuminated and facilitated by reference to modern educational practice whether through a formal course or a less structured approach.

Finally, employers and accrediting agencies must assume their responsibility in the matter of preparing college teachers. They must ask for good people, appropriately educated, and not ask merely that the new employee's degree add luster to the faculty roster. No combination of two or three letters attached to his name will automatically guarantee the success of a college teacher.

4. Who's Doing What?

A Survey of Preparation of College Biology Teachers in American Graduate Schools

This survey was initiated in response to an inquiry from a young graduate student who had reached a dead end at his own graduate school. He wanted to teach biology in a college after he received his Ph.D., but his training did not seem to be preparing him to fulfill his goals. He wanted to know from CUEBS where he would find someone with a program and someone who cared. This chapter should provide him and others who have the same problem with some answers, but he would be well advised to make some on-the-spot inquiries. Graduate institutions are large and complex and what is true of one part of a university is not at all guaranteed to be true of another.

The search was also stimulated by inquiries from faculty members and department heads who were actively seeking ideas and hoped to find worthy models to emulate.

The questionnaire developed in the search for answers to these questions was kept simple in order to add as little burden as possible to the department head, already overloaded with paperwork. The first mailing was sent to a college, a division, or a department of biology, if biology was organized on a unified basis, or to a department of botany and a department of zoology in universities with that type of organization. The problem of where to draw the line in sending to departments of genetics, anatomy, microbiology, etc., was handled in a very simple way. Those who filled out the questionnaires, addressed to departments of biology, botany, and zoology, were asked what other departments should receive a questionnaire. When someone indicated that a department would be likely to give a useful reply, a questionnaire was sent to that department.

Forms were sent to departments offering the Ph.D. and other graduate degrees—nearly 500 in all. All replies were studied for good ideas and many good ideas were received from departments offering terminal master's degrees. However, statistical treatment was limited to the 175 replies from departments or other units offering a Ph.D.-level degree. These departments grant 1,197 such degrees in a typical year. The response was very gratifying: 84% of the forms sent out were completed and returned. Those replying are listed in Appendix J. Their thoughtfullness was very much appreciated.

Try us again in three or four years. Hopefully, by then we will have something really good going.

Answer to a questionnaire

This report should give a good picture of *what* is being done to prepare college biology teachers, but it should not be quoted as a representative picture of *how much* is being done to prepare future college biology teachers. Unless the reader recognizes the design of the inquiry, he might arrive at far too sanguine a view of the current state of endeavors to that end, for those who are doing something were more likely to be asked for a report and were more apt to reply. Affirmative replies were computed in percentages of the total replies but weighted according to the number of Ph.D.s awarded annually.

Some respondents requested a blank questionnaire, presumably to use as a checklist. This might be the best possible use for the questionnaire.

EXPLANATION OF THE FIGURES GIVEN BELOW

1. The figure given is the percentage of Ph.D.s graduating in a typical year from departments which replied affirmatively to the question. For example, 105 departments out of 175 replied that they did rank their teaching assistants so that responsibility and perquisites increase with experience (11th item below). In all departments replying, 1,197 students graduated with Ph.D.s in a typical year. The departments replying affirmatively granted 723 Ph.D.s. Thus 60% (or 723/1,197) were recorded in the list below. It makes little difference in the rank order whether percentages were determined this way or by unweighted percentages of departments.

2. Answers are ranked below in order of affirmative replies.

MOST UNIVERSALLY PRACTICED BY RESPONDENTS

1. *Most of our graduate students gain experience teaching by acting as teaching assistants.*   99%

The fact that the experience as teaching assistant is the major tool for the preparation of college teachers is the reason the teaching assistant has received so much attention in the CUEBS conferences and in this report.

2. *Our teaching assistants have opportunity to engage in a variety of kinds of teaching experiences (lecture, laboratory, discussion).*   97%

Although almost all reported that the opportunity was theoretically available, very few reported that provision for a variety of experience was deliberately built into the program.

3. *All teaching assistants receive some kind of stipend.*   94%
One respondent was decidedly in the minority. He replied, in effect, "Absolutely not! Why should he be paid any more than a person taking practice teaching is paid?"

4. *Teaching assistants are closely supervised by a faculty member or senior teaching assistant charged with the course.*   93%
Many teaching assistants tell a different story. Some say they are thrown an outline of the laboratory and allowed to sink or swim.

5. *Teaching assistants have an opportunity to teach at various levels (not only the beginning course).*   92%
There are departments which have deliberately built into the program for teaching assistants an opportunity to teach at various levels as an important part of their education. In most cases, unfortunately, an affirmative reply means that a TA might teach at more than one level but more by chance than by design.

COMMONLY PRACTICED BY RESPONDENTS

6. *Teaching assistants have opportunity for continuing consultation about their teaching throughout the semester.*   83%
Eighty-three per cent claim this to be true in their departments. One must ask about almost one-fifth who thus seem *not* to have opportunity for continuing consultation throughout the semester. It seems hard to believe that such a situation could exist in a reputable institution, yet graduate students often report that they have no place to turn for criticism and help in their teaching. This is possibly the bitterest complaint of teaching assistants.

7. *All graduate students are required to serve as teaching assistants.*   77%
This can be viewed in two ways. Since most Ph.D.s in biology will teach, there is merit in requiring all to learn by being teaching assistants. Since the teaching assistant is presently the college teacher of a very large number of undergraduates, the quality of the university depends in good part on his performance. There are those who do not have the aptitude to be good teachers, for example, those who have difficulty speaking English. It is a fair question whether they should be inflicted on the beginning undergraduates.

8. *Our teaching assistants have opportunity to develop original materials and approaches.*   74%
In a few cases there is an active program to incorporate material developed by teaching assistants into the course. Teaching assistants in such places know that creative work is expected of them.

9. *We take steps to see that the prestige of a teaching assistant is the same as that of a research assistant.*   73%

Some went so far as to add that they find no need to take such steps because teaching assistants already have as much (or more) prestige. Some reported that they pay teaching assistants more than research assistants. This, of course, is rare.

10. *There is a ceiling on the contact hour load.*   70%

A typical contact hour load is 8–10 hours per week.

11. *We have ranked our teaching assistants so that responsibility and perquisites increase with experience.*   60%

Many reported that they do this informally.

12. *We have a definite program of orientation for our teaching assistants.*   55%

There seemed to be no relationship at all between the size of the institution and the answer to this question. One would expect that the larger the institution the more the need for a formal program.

INFREQUENTLY PRACTICED BY RESPONDENTS

13. *We supplement the teaching experience with a seminar or symposium on teaching.*   24%

The words "or seminars" were inadvertently omitted from the original questionnaire sent out. Since respondents were urged to edit the statements to make them fit the situation, some added the missing word. There was opportunity to comment on seminars in the unstructured section at the end. This oversight may have reduced the percentage of affirmative replies to the question somewhat but it seems not to have done so.

14. *We are engaged in an experimental program for preparation of college biology teachers.*   19%

The replies from those who replied affirmatively did indeed report evidence in support of this contention.

15. *Our graduate students are encouraged to take a modest amount of course work in teaching.*   14%

Some filled the page with exclamation marks and declared, "Never. Over my dead body!" Some indicated respect for their departments of education and acknowledged help they had received from them.

16. *Our department offers some degree at the Ph.D. level in which a creative activity related to teaching can be used as the thesis.*   13%

This opportunity most often is associated with the Ph.D. in Science Education or the plans for the Doctor of Arts although it is possible now to use such a dissertation for the Ph.D. in Biology and it seems that the trend is increasing.

17. *We supplement the teaching experience with a reading list on college teaching.*   6%

Reading lists were more often part of the materials prepared for a course rather than generally available.

18. *We have developed a handbook for teaching assistants.*   4%

Very few handbooks were received and most of these would not be useful to other institutions. See the model handbook in Appendix E.

19. *We have an extern program in which some of our students do some of their teaching in a different type of institution (such as a four-year or two-year college.)*

Less than 4% replied affirmatively.

The last page of the questionnaire was the most important—a blank page for making unscheduled reports of what the departments were doing. In some cases, rather highly publicized programs melted away completely when the respondents were asked for specific details. The questionnaire also revealed that some prestigious institutions have virtually no program to prepare future college teachers or even to supervise the institution of their own beginning students.

These quotations indicate the gravity of the situation:

> Too often our teaching assistants are selected from a pool of graduate students who have not been given a fellowship or traineeship or have not been supported by a research grant.

> In comparison with other forms of support, TA support is offered mostly to United States students with relatively weak academic records or to foreign nationals.

On the other hand, a number of worthy ventures were reported.

IDEAS WORTH CONSIDERING

CONFERENCES

Several departments have conferences for TAs before classes begin in the fall. These conferences are designed to orient new teaching assistants to their responsibilities. In some cases, they also provide an opportunity to examine objectives and to develop techniques of teaching.

The University of Colorado makes good use of consultants in a 3-day institute in the fall, followed by four monthly seminars. The emphasis throughout is on inquiry-oriented teaching. The description of the program appears as Appendix B of this work. Next year graduate students will develop their own laboratory activities and will try them out in regular laboratories during the year if all goes well.

Those who have participated in the conference at the University of Utah say that it gains great strength by being interdisciplinary. Participants are carefully selected and are paid $75 for attending the 3-day conference. Those who attend feel that one of the most valuable experiences of the conference is the microteaching experience. This will play an important part in the ambitious conference at the University of Montana this year. Here, too, the student participants will be paid for attending the week-long conference.

Kent State University will introduce a 2-day college teaching workshop in 1970 as part of a campus-wide effort. One day will be devoted to an all-university function and the other day will be spent in departmental activities organized by the departmental coordinators of college teacher training.

MINILESSONS

Televised lessons are used in the program of the fall conference at some universities;[1] others use this technique at other times. A common approach is to have the TA teach a minilesson (a brief portion of a lesson or a brief presentation of a single concept) and then analyze it alone, with a sympathetic mentor, or with a group of faculty and TAs. Sometimes the tape is stored to provide a "before and after" picture of the growth of the graduate student as a teacher.

The television camera is only essential if the teacher is to see himself in action. Actually, much is gained by careful analysis of a performance whether television is used or not. Some replies give the impression that too much attention is paid to relatively unimportant matters such as the odd mannerisms of the instructor rather than the vastly more important question: Did the instructor evoke real thought and response from the students in the class? In the Zoology Department of the University of Michigan, a split screen is sometimes used, recording the performance of the TA on one side of the film and the response of the class on the other. In this way whether the students are fighting to respond or to keep awake can be ascertained.

SEMINARS AND COURSES[2]

The various universities offer a whole spectrum of courses and seminars, some for credit, some not; some required, some not; some focused on the problems of a particular course being taught by TAs, some focused on teaching in general. It is common for TAs to meet with the member of the faculty in charge of a course to discuss what is to be taught the next week, to work together to solve the problems which have arisen, and to anticipate the problems which are likely to arise. Ideally, these sessions furnish a forum for instruction in teaching, using the actual problems and challenges as points of departure.

---

[1] Among them: Yale, Florida State, Utah State, the University of Rhode Island, the University of Colorado, and the University of Montana.

[2] See Appendix C.

Some faculty seek ways to have informal man-to-man sessions involving the "old pro" with learners (University of Iowa and Iowa State, for example). The course offered at the University of California at Davis is an example of more organized, formal instruction in teaching. At Colorado State, a seminar in teaching developed by the Zoology Department and open to the whole community was so popular that weekly attendance varied between 200 and 300. At the University of Nebraska, 90% of the animal science faculty voluntarily attends the annual teaching symposium held in the college.

REWARDING EXCELLENCE

There are various ways to reward excellent performance by TAs. At the University of Utah, the best are promoted to teaching associate. The University of Pittsburgh not only promotes the best TAs but increases their stipends $100 per term.

At many places the reward comes through increased responsibility. In the Botany Department of the University of Michigan and at Ohio State, Boston University, Clark University and other universities, senior TAs have an important supervisory role.

The best teaching assistants at the University of Washington are chosen to work with honors undergraduates and are challenged to use the opportunity to produce something special. At Wake Forest, senior teaching assistants act as research advisors to selected undergraduates, while at Oregon State the best TAs are in charge of a summer session botany course for high school teachers. There the accent is on how best to teach the material being studied. Selected TAs in the Zoology Department of the University of Michigan teach a summer course *in toto,* including supervision of TAs.

At the University of St. Louis, a planned lecture experience is worked out definitely so that each person has a carefully supervised and criticized lecturing experience. TAs at Stanford design new laboratory exercises and each person gives a lecture under supervision. In addition, a senior TA has the opportunity to offer a course to be submitted to the faculty for review like any other course and if that course is accepted, it is offered as part of the regular curriculum.

Externships (internships at cooperating institutions) : The University of Minnesota sends both graduate students and undergraduates to act as teaching assistants in junior colleges of the Minneapolis area. In the special program for preparation of teachers for two-year colleges at Texas Tech University, candidates are required to teach for a semester in an internship program at a cooperating junior college, but they are paid for their participation.

The EPDA fellows at East Carolina University spend 5 weeks

working with an experienced small-college teacher. During the last 2 weeks, they do independent but supervised work with students in laboratories, lecture, and special activities.

At Sam Houston State University, prospective two-year college teachers visit cooperating institutions and faculty from these institutions are used in seminars on the university campus. Extern programs exist at Central Washington State College, Murray State, Atlanta University, and other institutions, but it would seem that the whole idea could profitably be exploited at others.

DANFORTH PROGRAMS

The Botany Department of the University of Michigan has been cooperating with the Center for Learning and Teaching at the University and the Danforth Foundation on a program to improve preparation of college teachers. Their program is described in *Memo to the Faculty* No. 37, available at the Center for Learning and Teaching of the University of Michigan. At the University of Chicago, there are Danforth Tutors who are junior colleagues in all aspects of teaching an introductory course. They participate in planning the course and work right along with the faculty in development and presentation of the course.

The Foundation does not presently have plans to support new programs to improve preparation of college teachers, and Dr. Laura Bornholdt, Vice-president of the Foundation, reports that she does not know how long the moratorium will last.

SELECTION OF FACULTY

Dr. Beidleman from Colorado State reports that when members of his department interview a faculty member for employment, they ask him to teach some particular bit of a course, not give a seminar, but teach something at the beginning level. Such concrete expressions of concern by the consumer might well have a salutary effect on the performance of the producer.

FACULTY-STUDENT CONCERNS

Some people said, "We do not have anything truly innovative to be copied by anybody, but we are a small department and we try to get the professor and student together and work as a team. What can we write down that could be copied by someone else?" This kind of concern for teaching is something worth copying. The following are some quotations from some replies:

We have had closer contact than most departments. Graduate students for the most part belong to one member of the faculty, occupying a desk in his office; they are really almost teaching partners—Northern Michigan University.

The key seems to be a kind of close-knit informality. . . . —Microbiology at Iowa State

We start first-year TAs in a lab adjacent to that of a senior staff member who is assigned as the TAs mentor and supervises his teaching, criticizes his exams, etc.—Brooklyn College.

We are a very small graduate department . . . so that our teaching instruction of graduate students is more on the personal level than in a formal program—Clark University.

Our teaching program for college teachers is conducted largely on a personal basis between the TA and professor—Lehigh University.

CONCLUSION

Actually, it is difficult to determine through a questionnaire where future faculty members are being well prepared. The essential ingredient is not a special technique which lends itself to easy tabulation but some program which brings together a concerned mentor and a concerned student in an arrangement which provides a rich measure of meaningful experience and maximum interaction on matters that count.

5. Faculty for Four-year and Two-year Colleges

The university is the only institution where a future college teacher can earn his credentials. The faculty members in a university not only reproduce themselves in preparing people to take their place in the research-oriented university, they also prepare people to teach at other types of institutions. Overwhelmingly, the models to be emulated, the opportunities for prestige, even the opportunities for exciting intellectual venture are shaped by the fact that the successful man on the university campus is the man who is pre-eminent in the field of research.

The problem is that only a small part of the graduate school population will some day step into the boots of the old master. Most who continue in the field of education will teach in institutions which do not have production of research findings as a major goal. With over 1,000 two-year colleges enrolling about two million students in the United States at the present time and two-year colleges being established at the rate of more than one per week, it would take little imagination to see that someone is going to teach in a junior college.

Although the four-year undergraduate college enrolls a smaller percentage of the nation's freshmen, its personnel needs are no less critical.

One must ask whether those who will teach in undergraduate institutions will be adequately prepared for their life work. Of course, each future college teacher must seize his opportunities to make himself a good teacher—and such opportunities abound even under the most adverse conditions. (This is fortunate, for many presently learn to teach under the most adverse conditions.) Further, he must learn from experience and consider his preparation at the university just that: a preparation for continuing perfection of those skills which make him a good teacher. Nonetheless, the preparation of teaching faculty for two-year and four-year institutions is an important responsibility of the university and the responsibility should be discharged with honor.

Universities demand excellence in research, but they tolerate mediocrity in teaching.

DR. FREDERICK REIF
University of California, Berkeley
Berkeley Conference

The major mission of the four-year, liberal-arts college and the two-year college is not the discovery of new knowledge but the education of students. Success in these institutions can best be measured in graduates who have learned to think, to find pleasure in thinking, and to deal intelligently and effectively with the world in which they live.

Research in such institutions has a different function. It has an important place as a means of keeping the faculty and students in touch with the creative act of discovery. It gives an authentic note to science as a never-ending quest. It is through this involvement with research that faculty and students come to know science as a personal experience. If the published reports of research carried on at such institutions advance the frontier of human knowledge in biology, as is sometimes the case, so much the better. Teachers there need not chide themselves to note that this is usually not the case, for they have a different and no less important role to play in our society. Society will be in serious jeopardy if their job is not done well—better, in fact, than it is done now.

Faculty members at two-year and four-year colleges have a unique opportunity to engage in creative teaching and to apply the same genius to solving the problems of teaching as some apply to the investigation of photosynthesis or the origin of life. The problems are as challenging, certainly as complex, and unquestionably important. They will not be solved by the amateur, the dilettante, the routine practitioner of the art of teaching. Further, they will not be solved by the tired, badgered college teacher holding back with one hand the thousands of petty details that beset his professional life while with the other he tries to find a new way. The new and better under-graduate education will demand the best efforts of superior people working under conditions which make the discovery of a better way of teaching a goal recognized as being worthy.

The two-year and the four-year college have a unique opportunity in educational research and in the actual practice of good teaching. It should be unnecessary to explain to educated people the importance of education received in the undergraduate years, but many who have been slow to see undergraduate education as a vitally important component of our society have recently been persuaded to new concern university designed to reproduce university educators.

Again, the major question is whether the future teachers at two-year and four-year colleges need education they are not getting in a university designed to reproduce university educators.

A working group under the chairmanship of Dr. Stanley E. Gunstream at the CUEBS Berkeley Conference addressed itself to the question of how the special needs of two-year and four-year college teachers are best met. They concluded:

> Basically, the desirable fundamental teacher qualities are the same, regardless of the level of instruction or type of institution, but teachers in the two-year college must *really want* to teach and interact with students; and their *biological training must be broad-based*.

> Nearly all biological courses taught at two-year colleges are introductory courses. A program leading to the Ph.D. in Science Education such as the one offered at Berkeley would be extremely interesting for teachers in two-year colleges, but the majority felt that the Ph.D. is preferable and more acceptable, especially if teacher training is incorporated into the program.

> It was suggested that a modification of the dissertation research be made, not in rigor, but in emphasis, so that it may be more useful to the prospective teacher.

A major portion of their discussion concerned the need for an intern program (see below).

Dr. Willis Hertig, who wrote the CUEBS position paper *Biology in the Two-Year College* (Publication No. 26, April, 1969), in a recent talk on the subject concurred:

> Now is not the time for special graduate programs for the preparation of two-year biologists, but a time to encourage biology departments with graduate programs to relax their tight-fisted grip on the traditional Ph.D. program and to take a long and candid look at the nature of the responsibilities their graduates assume after graduation. By encouraging potential Ph.D.'s to take a block of pedagogically relevant experiences and by allowing research into biology education as a valid scholarly endeavor, I believe biology departments will more honestly meet the needs of those students who sincerely want to teach at the college level and who are intelligent enough to know that field and laboratory research as a way of life for the majority is a pipedream.

At the meeting of the AIBS-CUEBS National Task Force of Two-Year College Biologists where the Berkeley meeting was discussed, the consensus was that the current Ph.D. is not fulfilling the need of two-year college teachers and that two routes seem evident: development of a new degree or modification of the existing Ph.D. program.

The statement below was endorsed by the Task Force and subsequently by the Educational Committee of the American Institute of Biological Sciences.

1. The academic training for prospective two-year college biology teachers should be no different from the training for prospective four-year college biology teachers.

2. Basic to the doctoral degree should be comprehensive mastery of subject matter.

3. The doctoral program should include professional preparation in the areas of testing and evaluation, data analysis and interpretation of educational research; learning theory and educational psychology; curriculum development and innovations in teaching methods at the college level.

4. Practical exposure to the teaching profession should include a one-semester internship in college teaching under the guidance of fully qualified professionals.

5. The doctoral program should offer the student the option of preparing a dissertation in the subject matter field or in a recognized area of research and development in college teaching.

The methods of achieving the professional preparation suggested in Item 3 above were not specified in detail because there was no wish to be prescriptive. It is desirable that there be a rich choice of options. Some institutions and some students will take the route of formal course work; preparation might be achieved instead by seminars, independent study, or directed internships.

In June 1969, a Conference on Science in the Two-Year College was held in Washington, D. C. The recommendations which were prepared at that conference were subsequently adopted by the Commission on Undergraduate Education in the Biological Sciences and by the Education Committee of the American Institute of Biological Sciences on recommendation of the National Task Force of Two-Year College Biologists. They are also supported by the other professional societies represented at the conference. These recommendations are listed below in the form accepted by the Commission:

A. Each university science department with a graduate program preparing college teachers should recognize and accept responsibility for the preparation of college teachers of its discipline.

B. The broadest possible encouragement should be given for the development of innovative experimental programs leading to better trained teachers and for the careful study and evaluation of the results of those programs.

C. The minimum academic preparation for a two-year college science teacher should be equivalent in level to a master's degree *in the discipline* to qualify in the subject he teaches. Further academic training is highly desirable, and should stress breadth as well as depth.

D.   Appropriate preparation for the two-year college science teacher should include experience, supervised by a science department (preferably in the two-year college). This experience should provide knowledge of the kinds of students, the nature of the institutions, knowledge of materials, and methods for teaching the discipline.

The American Association of Junior Colleges makes this statement in its brochure on *Preservice Training of Two-Year College Instructors*:[1]

Considering the broad scope and plurality of objectives at "democracy's colleges," it seems both proper and inevitable that the methods and content of programs to prepare instructors also should be flexible and varied. Experimentation, diversity, and pragmatism are hallmarks of the community junior college movement. The same qualities should be evident in programs to provide professional preparation for its new faculty members.

They say further:

The Association agrees that heavy stress must remain on a quality graduate curriculum in the future teacher's major disciplinary field (s), whether academic or vocational.

Yet considering the expanded responsibilities of America's modern two-year colleges, there should and must be other important considerations in preparing their future teachers. The Association encourages multiple training models and approaches. However, it also recommends that preservice training of future faculty for its member colleges should include certain particular elements. Among the central factors to look for in a well-conceived preservice training program are:

The historical role of the two-year college and it future place in American higher education

Modern learning theory, including the uses and limits of educational evaluations, testing, and measurements

The theory and techniques of curriculum development

Elements of student guidance and counseling

Knowledge and practice in school administration, to make campus communications easier; facilitate teacher participation in campus governance and related activities; and help prepare faculty for administrative jobs later on

---

[1] A copy may be obtained from the Association, One Dupont Circle, Washington, D. C. 20036.

The profile, culture, goals, and values of the diverse student population at today's junior colleges

An opportunity for substantial, relevant supervised practice teaching or internship at a two-year college

Construction and use of programmed curriculum and other innovative instructional techniques

Handling modern media and "educational hardware," including its integration with traditional teaching methods

How to define, implement, and measure specific goals for student learning so as to reach clear, measurable learning objectives within a definite period of time

The ability to locate and apply resources to help define and meet the socioeconomic needs of a college and neighborhood. Actual work experience and involvement in a community project. Practical application of experience acquired to improve teaching and student communication

Interdisciplinary coordination of instruction in teaching "core" subjects, so as to reach students with widely different abilities, backgrounds, and goals.

Many of the items on this list will strike the reader as inappropriate to the Ph.D. It is certain that they will drive some readers to apoplexy. If taken literally, the list would exclude most Ph.D. programs as preparation for teaching in the two-year college.

While the factors listed as characteristic of a good program would be desirable in the preparation of many college biology teachers, it would be a mistake to force all junior college teachers into this mold. It would be a loss to the profession if standards of preparation and certification were to become so "professionalized" as to disadvantage those well grounded in subject matter and research in the discipline. The teaching community should not take this danger lightly.

The life work of the person who will continue at the university will differ in emphasis from the life work of the person who will be engaged at an undergraduate institution. Some at the university will have research as a sole responsibility; some college professors will be responsible solely for teaching. Most will be engaged in both research and teaching. Just as their major responsibilities differ in emphasis, their preparation might well differ in emphasis. This difference in emphasis should not obscure the fact that there are needs common to both the teacher and researcher.

At the risk of repeating some points made elsewhere in this volume, some of these needs should be listed. Both the teacher and the researcher must have a solid scholarly foundation; both must have experience in scientific investigation; both must have intelligence and an inquiring spirit.

The education of the future college teacher must have enough breadth so that he can teach an excellent beginning course, the ultimate test of a teacher of biology; the future specialist in some field of biology will deal with a narrower slice of knowledge but he, too, needs some breadth to maintain his perspective and to prevent foreclosing opportunities.

The future teacher needs some preparation in teaching—perhaps best a teaching experience enriched with seminars. Such experience (in some cases not as extensive) would not be amiss for the future university professor who probably will also teach some day.

Each should know first-hand about the kind of institution where he is likely to make his career. For the man who will stay at the university this is no problem: he is already learning on the job. The one who will leave the university for a teaching institution would do well to have an internship off campus to provide the insight he needs. A model internship is described in the next chapter.

Finally, it is imperative that the two-year college biology teacher be considered first and foremost a college biology teacher and a *two-year* college teacher second. Willis Hertig, in *Biology in the Two-Year College,* says

> The two-year college biologist feels estranged from the remainder of the biological community and apprehensive about his presumed second class citizenship in it. In essence, he does not feel that he is participating in the forward march of biology but rather that he is standing on the sidelines, with much of the action obscured from his view. It is the responsibility of the professional biological societies to see that two-year college biologists become actively engaged in the biological community.

A special program setting two-year college teachers apart as a special class is anathema to them, yet teachers in teaching institutions —two-year or four-year—must be prepared well as teachers for that is the business of such institutions. The solution is to be found in a diversity of opportunity and mobility across borderlines that is characteristic of American education and American society. There would seem to be a place in the broad spectrum of American two-year and four-year colleges for those with Ph.D.s, Doctors of Arts, Ed.D.s, as well as master's degrees and intermediate degrees.

Those who choose faculty members must choose the man for what he is, with due regard for his preparation and his potential, and not merely tally degrees.

6. A Model Cooperative Internship Program [1]

An internship may take one of several forms. It may be post-doctoral; it might take place, as at Yale, between the awarding of a Master of Philosophy degree and a Ph.D. Another model is the Michigan Scholars Program of the University of Michigan, under which teaching fellows take the place of a teacher on leave from a small college. It is most likely to consist of a teaching experience at a cooperating institution in place of part of the teaching-assistant experience normally conducted at the university. In any case, an internship at the appropriate undergraduate institution is one of the most neglected opportunities to better the preparation of college biology teachers.

The model which follows is not based upon any particular existing program. It is, rather, an ideal one and a very personal one compounded from the experience of many years of teaching at a four-year college and a year of intensive attention to the problem as a staff biologist at CUEBS. I should not be surprised if, unknown to me, such a model does exist somewhere; if it does not exist, it should. Perhaps someday it will.

An internship at an undergraduate teaching institution can provide unusual opportunities. The situation is life-size. The intern deals with a reasonable number of students who can be *his* students if he is successful as a teacher. The faculty is small enough so that the intern can enter into the life of the community appreciated and appreciative, but unawed. He can become part of a team, contributing to the common good and urged on by the other members of the team. The give-and-take and exchange of ideas can be exhilarating, particularly when enriched by the other influence on the intern: his access to the resources of the university.

Conditions are flexible enough so that patterns can be changed as old ideas are found wanting and new ideas emerge, and there is opportunity to try new approaches without great disruption of the system.

The intern can get a realistic picture of the challenges and opportunities of the kind of place where he may someday teach. There is so much to learn on the spot that cannot be learned any other way,

---

[1] Called an externship by some to distinguish it from an internship on campus.

for each type of institution has its own style, emphasis, and even folkways. A life of teaching in a college is a deeply satisfying experience for those who choose that challenge, but those who stumble into it uninformed or accept it reluctantly as a refuge from unemployment are apt to be unhappy. There is likely to be a rude adjustment for the person who comes to a small campus expecting to teach only when he is not busy with his research, or who expects to find the equipment magically set up in his laboratory when he opens the door.

I am almost certain that the time will come when all of our colleges and universities will have to think that course revision and keeping courses up to date is an essential part of the job, as essential a part of the annual budget as paying someone to do the actual classroom teaching.

DR. LYLE PHILLIPS, NSF
Washington Conference

Teaching in a small college is a respected profession. Those dedicated to teaching students may take as much pleasure in the growth of a new member of the profession as they do in the success of their students.

The ideal internship has these ingredients:

A well-educated student who looks upon the internship as a unique opportunity. (He should take an internship on another campus only by choice and only after he has done some supervised teaching at the university.)

A mentor who is himself a good teacher and who is actively engaged in an effort to make his course a better one. He looks forward to working with a junior colleague.

An atmosphere of inquiry and innovation. The student must be introduced early to the idea that a teacher's role is not just to dispense knowledge, but also to develop ways to facilitate learning.

A healthy mutualism in which the university and college, faculty members and students give freely of what each can best contribute and receive in return something which only the other can give. None is a suppliant. All give; all receive. It is essential to the model that the intern know that he is paying his own way, that he is repaying the very considerable effort spent to enrich his education with a service.

There are abundant opportunities to make the arrangement mutually advantageous. Since the intern will be well-informed in some narrow field of biology and is probably engaged in some exciting research, he will be splendidly equipped to give one or more seminar talks to the undergraduates and faculty in the department. The fact that *he* is the subject-matter expert will be very helpful in giving him the confidence needed as he develops skill in dealing with a student audience. Ideally, his own enthusiasm will be communicated to the undergraduates and this will do much to enlist their loyal support.

This is the ideal relationship: the intern brings fresh ideas into the department from the research frontier and serves as a model and inspiration to the undergraduates; at the same time he has the opportunity to develop his skills of presentation under the least threatening and possibly one of the most rewarding situations.

The intern will be well-equipped to guide the undergraduate research of at least one student, perhaps two, during the period of internship. Successful relationships would probably be continued by visits or correspondence when the intern returns to campus, and in this way the graduate student would have the chance to know the satisfaction of being a teacher and watching his student progress.

It is expected that the graduate student's university experience would give him fresh insights into the research problems of his undergraduate students. What he did not know might be developed from his circle of friends at the university. Who knows? The exchange might stimulate greater interest in teaching at the university. Links might develop between the university and the undergraduate college which have existed previously side by side without the slightest benefit to each other.

As part of his education, the intern should work with his mentor on one course, participating in all of its aspects. The professor would still be responsible for the course, but he should encourage a sense of sharing.

I should not speak of the teaching assistant as a prospective college biology teacher; he is currently a college biology teacher.

DR. DONALD G. HUMPHREY
Oregon State University
Washington Conference

This relationship would probably be very rewarding for the professor. One of the serious drawbacks of teaching in a small college is the professional isolation that can occur. Reading helps; professional meetings help; opportunities for rewarding interdisciplinary friendships and exchanges of ideas compensate in part; but the professional loneliness still is there. It would be refreshing to most professors at small colleges to have someone fresh from the frontier to talk to. Professors who are excited about their teaching are always anxious to share ideas with someone on that subject.

In the ideal situation, the intern would not just be the hired hand who grades all the tests; he would participate in the construction, administration, validation, and grading of the tests. He would not merely administer the laboratory program from an outline prepared by an absentee professor; he would participate, to the extent of his experience and ability, in the development of a plan for the laboratory and in the execution and evaluation of that plan. He should not be a stockman or janitor, but he should enjoy the services of support personnel available to the faculty member—no more, no less. If the faculty member at the particular college is obliged to set up his own laboratory, so should the intern; if the faculty member supervises a laboratory assistant, so should the intern. The intern should not be a newly acquired extra pair of hands, but it is not a service to him to get the false idea that faculty members at undergraduate institutions are waited on.

The intern and his mentor would consult on objectives and strategies of presentation of "their" course, and it should be understood that the intern will be expected to leave behind some legacy in the ongoing program. He would prepare some *original laboratory unit,* some new experiment, some original reading program, an A-T module, or other creative contribution uniquely his own. Nominally, this is to help repay the cooperating institution, but in reality it is to imbue the graduate student with a zest for educational experimentation and experience in developing something new. His sense of accomplishment would be enhanced if the contribution could be identified with his name and survive in the program until it is replaced by something with more merit.

As the intern develops skill and proves himself to be worthy of trust, he should be given more and more responsibility until, ideally, he is giving most of the lectures and directing most of the laboratories by the end of his tenure.

Since a person suitable to guide an intern will be one who cares very much what happens to his class, it would not be surprising for him to be reluctant to trust the neophyte to do what he can do better. Relations will be more of a partnership if the intern is sensitive enough to recognize this sense of responsibility on the part of the faculty member and respect his concern for his class. It will also help if the faculty member reminds himself constantly of his obligation to the education of the graduate student. The ideal advisor will steer a course between abandoning the student to his own devices while he attends to his other responsibilities and merely treating him as an observer.

There is provision in this model for the graduate student to observe a college in operation. He should be welcome at staff meetings and faculty meetings and in the classes of other members of the department. He should be free to learn all he can from them, but he should have the responsibility of only one course lest his energies be dissipated by too many masters. If his time does permit him to attend faculty committee meetings and other campus activities, he will understand better how a faculty member spends his time.

He should have a faculty office if one is available or, if it is necessary, discover for himself that some faculty members must share offices. He should have the other perquisites of faculty members: football tickets, a parking place, and chance to sit in the hot sun in a cap and gown and listen to the president speak—if that goes with the job. It is even conceivable that an intern at a four-year undergraduate college might want to visit a nearby two-year college.

The internship should last at least a full quarter or semester. If the term of the university is longer than the term of the college, so much the better. This will make available some time for orientation and planning. The intern in residence will want a program which engages him full time—except for keeping up with his professional literature and perhaps preparing for a language examination. The commuting intern might possibly keep some of his research going at a reduced level. These arrangements would have to be worked out on an individual basis, keeping in mind that this is a unique opportunity which can only be useful if given the whole-hearted attention of the student.

The performance of the intern should be reported to the university and be a part of his record. Such information would be invaluable in writing meaningful recommendations. The intern would be expected to evaluate his experience so that the university could use informed judgment in deciding whether to send another student into the same situation.

There are always practical problems to be solved. For the intern, there is a problem of taking time out from his studies and research. It should be pointed out, however, that most graduate students already take at least this much time out for teaching. If the experience is worthwhile, it deserves a place in his program.

The graduate student will possibly need some substitute for the financial support he is receiving at the university. It may be that the resources of the university need to be supplemented by foundation support if they cannot be stretched to accommodate this added strain. Those who approach the National Science Foundation for such financial encouragement are well-advised to have a plan for improving the education of the graduate student and the undergraduates and not merely ask for money to perpetuate what already exists.

For some there will be problems of transportation and dislocation of living to overcome. This will be particularly easy to arrange for those who are at universities near suitable undergraduate colleges—a rather ordinary circumstance. It will be particularly difficult for graduate students supported by working wives if they have to spend a term at an isolated college. The college, if it is in a position to do so, might well make available a room for a quarter or semester as a contribution to the support of the program.

It will take effort and, in some cases, financial support to work out details of a successful internship, but potential rewards are high. A good program can introduce a new self-consciousness to the undergraduate college. It can engage the student in the real business of teaching in a place where teaching is an everyday concern and where he can work with his own limited group of students, where his efforts will receive individual attention. Finally, such a venture, once begun, would surely open unsuspected opportunities for advantageous cooperation among institutions. It seems reasonable to predict that each will gain new respect for the other as an added bonus.

7. And Finally . . .

There is change in the wind and some of this change is sure to be reflected in better preparation of college biology teachers. Some of the impetus for change comes from external events whose scope and implications are still the subject of debate, speculation, and a great deal of midnight musing. Much of the change is from within, the consequence of the continuing search for a better way.

One significant change is brought about by the current dislocation between supply and demand in employment. The dearth of opportunities for employment in research is causing applications for jobs to pile up on the desks of chairmen of departments in institutions devoted almost exclusively to teaching. The question arises whether applicants who prepared specifically for research are also prepared for the teaching job they will do. It is also interesting to ask whether this change in demand will refresh the teaching institutions with more able, if less prepared, faculty members. Finally, it will be interesting to learn whether the discrepancy between expectation and reality will frustrate the former researcher or whether he will be intrigued by the unsuspected challenges of grappling with undergraduate education.

One participant at the New England Conference said of the employment question: "It is not that there is a glut of biologists at present. There just is not enough demand for people who want to teach one course to twelve graduate students every year and spend the rest of their time on research."

Whether the present fragile market for research-oriented Ph.D.s is a temporary or long-term phenomenon or whether the problem is exaggerated or as serious as some say, it has caused new interest in the preparation of college teachers.

Undergraduate students and graduate students are asking as never before that their studies be meaningful, that they have a chance to deal with a real world and significant aspects of it. The better students are not content with routine performance. At the same time that there is a rising tide of expectation for the quality of education, there is a counter current making it vastly more difficult to raise the standard. With higher education now established almost as a right rather than a privilege, with higher education not restricted to those of a scholarly bent or to those able to pay their way, enormous challenges confront the academic world.

Public institutions must find a way to deal effectively with the huge numbers descending upon them and still treat each person as an important, unique individual. Private institutions must find ways to present the kind of education they hoped to present without being choked to death in the financial squeeze. Both will have to wrestle with the problem of educating members of a diverse population, many of whom do not fit the traditional mold. Reform and innovation in education necessary to meet these challenges will require faculty able to cope with new situations.

We have spent too much time learning to polish the stage coach door and not enough time developing new modes of transporation.

DR. RICHARD HARBECK
U.S. Office of Education
at the Washington Conference

Educational technology holds much promise for achieving the disparate goals of teaching more students and at the same time treating them like people. In actual practice, educational technology is still in an elementary stage and it is often badly misused. Graduate students are aware that technology will have a place in the world of education and they are worried about how they are to gain access to some of the techniques needed to make use of new opportunities afforded by new technologies.

Despite the popular rhetoric of disparagement, there *are* new approaches to teaching, newly defined goals, and new examination of values. Many of these innovations have reached higher education from work done at the lower levels, particularly in the elementary school. It would be a pity for graduate students to leave the university to teach without becoming aware of the newer trends to which their future students will be exposed before they get to college.

Teaching assistants and graduate students in general are more assertive and less tolerant of the system than formerly. Conditions that until recently would have been accepted as the lot of the graduate student are no longer accepted passively. Grievances of teaching assistants should be redressed because it is the right thing to do, not out of fear that unredressed grievances bear the seeds of revolt. Polarization of the academic community must not occur, for if those who must be partners in research and in education are forced into adversary roles, freedom of inquiry, zest for the cause, and the more attractive features of college teaching will be in serious jeopardy. Nonetheless, the more aggressive stand of the graduate student *is* one factor causing some to re-examine the question of college teacher preparation at their institutions.

Is this pressure for change making a difference in the preparation of college teachers? Yes, we see it from a national vantage point. Students are writing in for help in selecting a university—not for help in getting in, but to learn what university does the job in preparing its graduates to be better college teachers. Foundations are taking an active part in directing the search for better preparation and in influencing the reward system to make the teaching component of education more attractive.

Those hiring graduate students for teaching have not been very vocal in expressing their needs, but as opportunity to be selective increases, as it surely will, it is clearly predictable that their wishes will be expressed and considered.

Significant changes are under consideration at some universities commonly in a position of leadership. Many of these changes are still in the planning stage and it would be presumptuous to discuss them here. As these proposed changes under study now are introduced, competitive departments will surely want to be involved in the change. This all adds up to a new hope for better teaching of college biology.

Lest we seem too sanguine, it should be pointed out that if by some unimaginable miracle all of the problems of the preparation of college teachers were to be solved and each graduate stepped out with his shiny new degree in hand, fully equipped to do a splendid job of teaching biology, there would still be much to do to assure the best possible education for college students. One would not, like Philip of Macedonia, cry for want of worlds to conquer. There would still remain the thorny problem of keeping the faculty member fresh on the job.

The new graduate is just beginning his education. Unless he is extraordinarily able and takes extraordinary steps to fight off the forces of obsolescence, he will find that while he is growing in wisdom and experience, the information he carried away from graduate school is becoming a smaller and smaller part of what he should know. The dullards will not know the difference or will not be unduly exercised if they do. But the conscientious are embarked on a lifelong endeavor to renew and replenish what they know. The present system does not come to grips with the issue; the waste of human resources is staggering.

Some people, caught up in the American custom of trading in the old car rather than maintaining it in road-worthy condition, are content to rely upon a constantly replenished supply of college teachers. They find far less satisfaction in helping the established teacher keep the freshness and vitality needed for good teaching while he devotes his energies to service at the expense of his personal learning. There are faults in this idea that need to be weighed. First, the obsolescence of a faculty member *who is not constantly renewed* is faster than generally supposed. Some are already in a well-advanced stage of obsolescence in certain areas of their competence when they graduate from the university.

Another fault with this approach is that the enormous resources represented by the able, experienced faculty members are too valuable to toss aside, even if practical consideration were to outweigh the human and ethical considerations.

The problem is particularly acute in the undergraduate colleges—two-year and four-year alike——although obsolescence is not unknown at universities! Heavy loads of teaching and quasi-administrative duties and the isolation from colleagues at the research-front of the discipline conspire to keep the college teacher constantly running to keep abreast of the rapidly changing new material in the field.

This is not the place to repeat the well-known and well-documented descriptions of the enormous task of keeping up. The words torrent, flood, cascade, avalanche are usually used to conjure up the picture of what the conscientious college biology teacher faces in his efforts to keep abreast of developments.

Suffice to say that in a field as rapidly changing as biology a person without help could easily spend 100% of his working hours keeping abreast of the developments in the broad front necessarily covered by a person teaching undergraduates. Clearly this will not do, and it will not do for the college teacher to carry the burden of knowing that 100% of his effort is not enough. He needs help.

A program of constant refreshment should be built into his regular assignment. Part of every year should be set aside for refresher activities, starting with his first year of teaching. Each person should have a regular and careful diagnosis of his most urgent needs to determine what action would open new vistas to him, to remove barriers to his development, and to keep him abreast of developments in biology and in teaching. A catch-as-catch-can program just will not do. There should be a mechanism for filling the "prescription" but at present such opportunities are not well adapted to the need.

It would be a worthy challenge to the large universities, foundations, states, and biological societies to pioneer in the search for a radical new way to provide the college teacher with an opportunity to stay fresh. It should be a way that allows the college teacher to participate with dignity, not as a subject of a crash program of rehabilitation or a program for academic mendicants. A way could surely be found to make use of the talents of the college teacher to make the program one of mutual benefit.

States should give serious thought to making such a program part of the mission of the state universities and giving them additional financial support to make it worth their while. It would seem reasonable that state institutions might be assigned this new role which would do so much to raise the level of college education, public and private. It might contribute to better distribution of undergraduate enrollment in the institutions of the state.

Foundations would find it a very rewarding project to encourage pilot programs, to encourage innovative people to develop new means of diagnosing needs, and to devise special opportunities for refreshment which do not even exist now. Actually, it would seem that such activities would fall within the scope of some foundation programs already existing.

The challenge should extend, too, to the faculty member and to the institution which employs him.

It is inappropriate and even impossible to spell out in detail the solutions needed. That is a major project. Since CUEBS, with its short tenure remaining, can not undertake such a project, it is to be hoped that the Office of Biological Education, the Center for Biological Education, or some other agency will do so.

The preparation of better college biology teachers is urgent business. But the other unfinished business is the equally important job of providing for the constant refreshment of the college professor on the job. There is evidence that something is being done about preservice preparation; let us hope that the next step will be the development of schemes presently not existing even in dreams to help the man on the job grow in his work as long as he lives.

If there is anything else that we can do in a conference like this it is to resolve that some of the things that everyone knows *ought to get done get done.*

DR. WALTER D. KNIGHT
University of California, Berkeley
Berkeley Conference

---

8. Appendices

A. MODEL PROGRAMS FOR TEACHING ASSISTANTS

WORKING GROUP A
Berkeley Conference

PARTICIPANTS: Allen, Anderegg, Copeland, Davis, Hague, Harris, Hildebrand, Palmblad, Savage, Winokur. Sanford S. Tepfer, *Chairman*.

A. Attitudes toward teaching
 1. The contribution of the teaching assistant must be recognized throughout the institution and department as an important part of the system.
 2. He should have opportunity for full participation. He should be required to prepare and give lectures, participate in course planning, help write and grade examinations. He must share in the responsibility for the course.
 3. Potential as a teacher should be considered in hiring of TAs. Those recommending them should be asked to rate their potential as teachers. Those who will not be competent teachers should not be chosen.
 4. Teaching duties must be integral to the Ph.D. program—not merely peripheral. The professor supervising the student must recognize that teaching is important. He should allow the student to become fully involved in his teaching.

B. A special training course
 1. Attention should be given to general matters that apply to all courses: how to hold discussions, write examinations, and give grades. "Pat" techniques should be avoided. The teaching assistant needs to develop confidence in himself.
 2. Teaching assistants should be exposed to high quality models—in person and via videotape. Former successful TAs should be taped in action. The professor should run a laboratory to show how he does it. The TA should be videotaped for analysis of his program.
 3. Information on various new methods should be presented—audio-tutorial laboratories, computer assisted instruction, TV lectures, and others which may not presently be in use at the university. Through demonstration and criticism, the TA should come to know the limitations of various techniques.
 4. Help from the School of Education should be sought. It can help in the evaluation of our methods and tell us how to achieve certain competencies we desire.

5. Validity, not just reliability, in instruction and testing should be emphasized.

6. The TA should get some information that will help him when he is asked by students for personal advice: fainting, suicide, etc.

C. Training and prep sessions

1. There should be weekly prep sessions to discuss objectives and the progress of discussion sections and laboratory sections.

2. The teaching assistant must learn to do laboratory preparations, but he must not be burdened with routine repetitive work. He should be provided support personnel. The professor should participate with the TAs in preparations.

3. The teaching assistant should be asked to evaluate the course, the professor, and his own performance.

4. Every professor in every course should hold regular sessions with his TAs to maintain a constant feedback.

5. The new TA should have help from an experienced person in planning his first performance.

D. Original performance

1. Teaching assistants should be encouraged to take responsibility to innovate. They should try new and better laboratory materials—possibly on an experimental group.

2. Teaching assistants in small groups should be encouraged to plan and offer a full-length course or minicourse of 1 or 2 weeks.

3. They should lead the undergraduate into the library and give him help in how to use it.

4. They should run evaluation sessions with their own students. They should seek immediate feedback under unthreatening circumstances from peers, from the professor, and from students via comment boxes, etc.

WORKING GROUP A
Michigan Conference

PARTICIPANTS: Anderson, Costello, Daniel, Hagerman, Husband, Nisbet, Thompson. Gerson M. Rosenthal, *Chairman.*

Our group was in remarkable agreement as to what should be done, at least at the level of principle, and very likely could produce a fairly complete model were our universities more similar and if our product and its market were more uniform. We simply recognize that the interests, needs, and career goals of graduate students are variable; departmental emphases also differ.

To simplify this summary, I will make the debatable assumption that our universities are committed to producing, in adequate numbers, the best possible teachers of undergraduates. This assumption permits us to duck the issue of the conventional research-oriented Ph.D. program versus the instruction-oriented graduate program by suggesting that there might be some relaxation of the usual thesis requirements in those instances when it makes sense to do so. This is not to suggest relaxation of standards for a second-class student or program but rather the introduction of intelligent flexibility.

Our model, then, calls for two obvious kinds of personnel: faculty and graduate students.

1. We need some number of faculty members who are able, committed, and desirous of devoting the necessary time and energy to teach undergraduates and to the education of graduate students who may continue this commitment. Further, and perhaps more important, it requires that those faculty members not so involved recognize that such activities are not only necessary but honorable and deserving of recognition and support, both moral and substantive.

2. We need the participation of all graduate students—or at least most of them, for one can conceive of a few students for whom experience as a TA would be traumatic to all involved. I choose to overlook the obvious fact that we must use most graduate students simply to get our teaching job done but would emphasize the view that some teaching experience will, at least, require an increased mastery of subject matter, may provide that sample of experience that influences choice of career, and is, of course, an absolute necessity for those whose intent is to become strongly involved with undergraduate teaching.

More specifically, our model is concerned primarily with the doctoral candidate since there is more time available for his education and training and because it seems likely that some kind of doctorate will more and more become a requirement for teaching at all levels beyond the high school.

We propose the following:

1. All graduate students should serve as teaching assistants for a minimum of one year, preferably two or even more if they wish. This will permit assistants a more complete experience by beginning at the bottom with work in the prep room and gradually moving from aide and observer to true teaching assistant, primarily in the laboratory, and ultimately to leader of discussion sections and occasional lecturer (this sequence should be less rigid than the listing suggests).

2. Instruction of assistants with regard to specific handling of laboratory and discussion sections is the major responsibility of the faculty. Frequent meetings, probably weekly, are necessary and require prior preparation on the part of both faculty and assistants. These sessions should provide not only review of the subject matter at a level appropriate to the interest of the assistant and to the understanding of the student, but the opportunity to raise questions of scientific and pedagogical interest, the latter ranging as broadly as possible. Some of the panel feels that some or much of this instruction may be advantageously handled by a senior predoctoral student who is well acquainted with all aspects of the course (serving as the faculty deputy) and who may be closer to the assistant both in time and attitude than is the instructor. In any case, final responsibility for this instruction rests with the faculty member.

3. Some sort of program, possibly a seminar, should be required of all assistants. This program should be planned by biology faculty and should be concerned with methods, philosophy of teaching, curriculum

and course construction, educational goals, course and teaching evaluation. The knowledge and talents of all appropriate faculty members, including those outside of biological departments, e.g., those in mathematics and statistics, education, psychology and philosophy should be exploited. Course credit for this discussion is desirable and probably necessary.

4. Interested students should be encouraged, but not required, to take courses offered in other departments that may broaden horizons or lead to increased professional competence or outlook.

5. As assistants mature, they should be encouraged to make constructive criticisms of the courses in which they are teaching, propose exercises, discussion topics, and changes or additions to subject matter coverage as their expertise and experience suggest.

6. The performance of assistants should be evaluated in writing, at least briefly, and verbally in conference between faculty and TA. This is for the benefit of the TA and is quite different from the kind of statement one writes in letters supporting job applications. If course credit for assisting is given (discussion indicates that this is presently uncommon), whether as inducement or reward, honest grades should be assigned—faculty members should feel no compunction in grading down a student who does not perform satisfactorily or shows poor attitudes toward his teaching obligations. Senior assistants are effective evaluators and student response, via well constructed questionnaires (or even less formal feedback), is also useful.

7. Departments or larger administrative units should consider hiring a specialized faculty member whose prime function will be to develop programs of instruction, both as regular curriculum and special training of assistants (who are our future faculty members). This is not a simple issue, particularly at highly research-oriented institutions.

The foregoing is oriented toward the teaching of introductory biology courses. We also recommend assisting experience at the upper division course level; such experience involves modifications of the model for emphasis on the preprofessional training of undergraduates and includes a close working relation of a faculty member and one or a small number of assistants as a reduced course enrollment demands.

What we propose may be profound and elegant or platitudinous and frivolous depending on your view. There is probably no best model—but certainly there are bad ones. Speaking for myself, I have a firm faith in the ability, seriousness of intent, and good will of the young graduate student. My faith in the faculty is less profound but buoyed up considerably by what I have heard in these sessions. Ultimately, the faculty will shape up whether from a true awareness of the importance of the teaching function, enlightened self-interest, or through external pressure from students (which is already strong), administrators, legislators, and the general public.

B. MODEL INSTITUTE

A Workshop to Train Graduate Students for College Teaching

DAVID O. NORRIS
Department of Biology, University of Colorado

More than two-thirds of those receiving doctorates in the biological sciences enter college teaching with the majority teaching lower division undergraduate courses (*CUEBS News*, June 1968). At the University of Colorado, more than 90% of those who receive advanced degrees in Biology enter the teaching profession and a large proportion accept a large introductory course as their primary teaching responsibility. The workshop idea was born from reflection upon our own training and from these observations at the University of Colorado which we believe reflect the national scene:

1. Advanced degree recipients have had little or no practical insights into teaching strategies. They are neither acquainted with the programs of the Biological Sciences Curriculum Study (BSCS) nor are they familiar with the Commission on Undergraduate Education in the Biological Sciences (CUEBS) and its involvement in the undergraduate biological education.

2. They lack teaching experience or their "teaching" experience has been as laboratory "policemen."

3. Their training has been directed toward content memorization and narrow research programs.

4. In general, new college and university teachers simply employ the traditional approaches by which they were taught.

Last fall we attempted a mini-institute prior to the beginning of the fall semester and then provided ample pre- and post-laboratory time throughout the semester for the graduate teaching assistants to "experiment" with the techniques and ideas to which they had been exposed. The response of the graduate teaching assistant and the undergraduates was such that we decided to go ahead with the program on a larger scale, providing additional opportunity for gaining broader involvement on the part of the graduate students. Next year we will offer a program in teaching techniques and strategies for our graduate teaching assistants. Instruction will be provided in concepts and techniques suitable for application to improvement of undergraduate education in the Biological Sciences. We will utilize people from various departments on the campus to implement the program. Considerable emphasis will be placed upon teaching in the laboratory because the laboratory offers a small group with which the graduate teaching assistant can work comfortably. All of these techniques can be applied to the "lecture approach" as well.

Prior to the beginning of each semester we will hold an intensive 3-day session covering the following topics:

1. Philosophy of Teaching Biology at the University of Colorado.

Reprinted from *CUEBS News*, Feb. 1970.

2. Advances in Biology Teaching.
   This topic entails questioning present teaching practices as well as a discussion of the investigative approach to teaching content and processes of science.

3. The Preparation of Learning Objectives.
   Includes the writing and evaluation of objectives by the graduate students.

4. The Noninvestigative Laboratory Experience.
   The participants will perform a laboratory exercise in the traditional sense.

5. Investigative Approach to the Laboratory.
   The participants will perform the same laboratory exercise in an inquiry-oriented manner.

6. Role of the Pre- and Post-Laboratory Experiences.
   A discussion of the importance of setting the scene for the learning experience (pre-laboratory) and the distillation of what the students have done and its significance (post-laboratory).

7. New Advances in Audio-Visual Media.
   Includes orientation of facilities available at the University of Colorado as well as demonstrations.

8. Criteria for Writing Laboratory Investigations.
   Includes an assignment of preparing one different laboratory per participant for later discussion and eventual implementation.

9. Teaching for Inquiry with Films and Slides.
   The participants will serve as a class and be exposed to this learning situation. They will have the opportunity to employ these techniques in the laboratory.

During each semester, we will hold four full-day sessions at monthly intervals dealing with the following topics:

1. Systems Analysis Approach to Improvement of Undergraduate Instruction.
   After a discussion of the approach, the participants will examine a lower division course and develop a program for systematic improvement. They will examine the criteria for and prepare a model biology curriculum.

2. The Audio-Tutorial Approach to Teaching: An Assessment.
   This will entail an explanation of the Postlethwait (Purdue) system and its possible applications to all levels and types of courses. The participants will gain some practical experience in writing programmed materials.

3. Teaching Biology to the Nonmajor. /
   The participants will each prepare and evaluate a course outline for a model nonmajor course.

4. A Critical Analysis of Evaluation Devices and the Preparation of Effective Test Items.
   The participants will gain experience in preparation of test items which can be tested for validity. These items will be based upon previously prepared learning objectives.

In summation, our graduate teaching assistants will be engaged as students, as observers, and as teachers in various aspects of the program. They will become acquainted with the mechanics of handling large numbers of students and techniques in organization that will free the instructor for maximal student contact and innovative teaching. Their regular teaching assignments will afford them an opportunity to experiment with the concepts and materials provided by the program. We hope they will graduate with an awareness, some skills, and a backlog of materials that will enable them to begin their professional teaching careers successfully in their first semester as new faculty members.

C. MODEL SEMINAR

Problems in Teaching College Biology

RICHARD V. BOVBJERG
University of Iowa

Most graduate students in biology have shared my own experience: the days and nights were filled with courses, seminars and research, and many additional hours were spent as a teaching assistant in the laboratory. Characteristically, we had no courses in education—a point of pride with most of us. Some were better instructors than others; they thought more about teaching and put more effort into it. We had, of course, the customary sessions with the professor for guidance in the coming week's work. Quite properly, the consuming interests were our own research and the classroom and corridor topics of the day. Our teaching was necessary for our support and, to many of us, was a chore.

Later, I, like most, was plunged into a position where teaching was my primary occupation. Unlike most, it was my own extreme good fortune to teach in a general biology course with a master teacher, Thomas S. Hall. Also unlike most, I had a very light teaching load during my first year. Still, suddenly and alarmingly, I was faced with decisions about course content, lectures, laboratories, and examinations. My graduate education had equipped me with the current notions in biology and a strong desire for inquiry, but had not prepared me for teaching. This is the usual dilemma, much discussed and much ignored.

Tom Hall, not satisfied with routine briefing of graduate assistants, had insisted that the staff meet to probe more deeply into just what we thought our course should do and what it was doing. From his fortunate graduate assistants of those days have come some outstanding teachers.

After moving to a new position, I perpetuated this form of graduate education. It is this experience that is reported here. No proposal is made for others; this must be a personal venture. Obviously the professor of such a seminar would be a serious teacher; no two such courses could be alike.

NATURE OF THE SEMINAR

The major aim of this seminar is the anticipation of the problems that will arise when the students have their initial, actual teaching experience. This has meant that my first role is not the transmission of my own experiences and emergent bias. The sessions are therefore as Socratic as possible, my own contributions coming only after those of the students. I am convinced such teaching is possible only in an informal environment, far from lecture podia, blackboards, and slide projectors. Our solution to this problem is having the class in the family living room, with free beer and pretzels. I have assured an A for the semester to anyone who speaks at least once; all earn this grade in the first five minutes! They are henceforth free to express opinions contrary to those they assume to be the professor's. We meet every other week for as

Reprinted from *CUEBS News*, Oct. 1968.

long as the session is profitable. Registration has ranged from 5 to 15; the latter number is at the upper level for free discussion.

Additional members of the departmental staff have contributed to the meetings. However, one must know his colleagues before inviting them to participate in such sessions. Men of very strong convictions and predilections to lecturing may hinder the desirable free flow of ideas and debate. Having two staff members also allows one of them to advocate for the devil and encourage the same among the students.

Since most of the graduate students teach in the larger general biology courses and since it is here that the greatest problems abide, we have usually restricted our discussions to the teaching of such courses. However, from time to time, we have tackled the problems of the undergraduate curriculum and upper-level courses, even to a critical review of our own offerings and program.

COURSE OF THE SEMINAR

THEORETICAL PROBLEMS

At our first meeting, I attempt to establish the dicta that an educator must have a reason for everything he does and that he must also have an overall philosophy of education. The first question asked is whether general biology should be a part of the required undergraduate program. Few of our graduate students have considered this question, and they are unable to defend their usually positive positions. We go on to ponder the role of biology in general education. It is not difficult to bend the student's phrases into one of Tom Hall's alliterations. "Freshmen come to us in biology: ignorant, illogical, illiterate and indifferent." We can then usually agree that the role of the biology teacher is to add to freshmen's knowledge of biology, increase their capacity for scientific thinking, enhance their ability to read carefully and critically, and excite them with living things and ideas about living things. The first evening gets long!

We then pose the question of how one does these things in a biology course. In the past, I have assigned readings to be discussed during the next two or three sessions. Too often this has meant selecting parts of books best read from cover to cover. I intend to rely more in the future on shorter papers, many of which have been emerging recently in *BioScience* and CUEBS Bulletins.[1] I shall certainly have the group read the CUEBS Publication No. 15, Biology in a Liberal Education. The chief virtue of discussing specific papers lies in the diversity of views and problems presented. The student is quickly disabused of the idea of a "best way" of doing anything. Most acquired a humility about their own narrow views. Comparing and attacking is also much easier than creating. I have found that even reticent graduate students often emerge in free-wheeling discussion of other people's outrageous notions.

Calling for conclusions ends this action of the seminar. What is a good course, a teacher, text, lecture, laboratory, examination? A useful device here is to ask each student who was his best teacher and why. By now the notion of a philosophy of education has become apparent, and some show evidence of creating their own. Sharp lines of disagreement often are evident in the group.

---

[1] Listings appended.

PRACTICAL MATTERS

In the last half of the semester, we try to test our ideas with specific problems. At these meetings, each student does some writing, which he duplicates for each member of the seminar. This forces each person to actually formulate notions in writing, in somewhat the same way he will as a teacher. The group then criticizes a few of these writings. We write (1) a course outline, (2) a lecture, (3) a laboratory exercise, and (4) an examination, and each of these is the subject for an evening's discussion.

COURSE OUTLINE

An outline for an elementary biology course is written by each student as though that course would be given next year. Students are asked to be specific about lecture titles, laboratories, etc. This is often a test of how open-minded the class has become after our theoretical discussions. Some clearly adopt the format of a current course or a text; others reveal some imagination. The session at which we discuss these outlines forces the authors to parry questions such as "Why did you assign two weeks and three labs to embryology but only one lecture to plant development?" Invariably this session ends with consideration of the role played by the several teaching tools. Is the lecture the prime source of information? Should the first experience be in the laboratory, followed by expansion in the next lecture? What is the best use of a text? Should the first course stress content or method? Should it cover or penetrate? This is usually another long session marked by many sparks of disagreement!

The group now selects a small portion, i.e. development homeostasis, etc., of an elementary course for more detailed planning. Lectures, laboratories, and examinations are constructed for this topic. Again, the writings are duplicated for all to read and criticize.

LECTURE

Constructing a single lecture is the first assignment. By now the instructor in the seminar is delighted at the barrage of questions. "Why did you start your first lecture on genetics with Mendel rather than meiosis?" "What is the major point of the lecture?" "You have too many details and not enough concept," or vice versa. "Would the class have had a laboratory on meiosis prior to this lecture?" "It is too long to do in one hour!" The lectures are not presented as such, but the discussion goes from particular criticisms to general notions of what a lecture can do or should be able to do and what it cannot do. (I inevitably unload my own bias on this subject by the end of the evening.)

LABORATORY EXERCISE

Designing a laboratory exercise is the most challenging of the tasks in the seminar. These are written as though they were ready to be printed and given to a class in general biology, with specific directions, materials, and questions. Some very dull exercises as well as some very sprightly ones have been presented. Often the laboratory instructions have a topic but no real purpose. "Why even have a laboratory on this topic?" Such general questions give way to more specific ones. "Are the pollen grains on slides or are they to be taken from live material?" Neither type of question can be ignored by the writer of a laboratory exercise. There is a tendency for graduate assistants to be very professionalistic about laboratories; they call for many drawings, complex apparatus, and a raft of technical terms. This can be challenged on theoretical as well as practical bases. This session always ends with a consideration of the value of laboratory teaching. I may take both positions: that they are not needed in an elementary course or that they should be the primary learning experience. Graduate students tend to take laboratory work for granted.

EXAMINATION

Our last session of the seminar is given to criticism of examination questions written by the group, on a selected topic. To make the transition from taking an examination to writing one is often humiliating; while students are experts at criticizing questions, they seldom are skilled in writing them. When we discuss the values of essay questions and laboratory examinations, we restrict our writing to objective questions. These are very difficult to construct, yet most of these students will be writing such questions in earnest very shortly. The group is quick to spot ambiguities and poor wording, but more time is needed before they ask the more important question of whether that item is worth asking or if it reflects the aims of the instruction. Now the emerging philosophy of education of each student is on the block. No matter how earnest these students were earlier in the seminar on outlining a "concepts" course, they tend to write purely fact-recall questions, often centering on terminology. We end this session by attempting to see how many types of questions were written; the instructor can usually supply many more. Perhaps in future seminars we can take a look at the CUEBS test item booklet.[2]

In all of these specific aspects of teaching lecture, laboratory, and examination, I attempt to allow the class to lead in criticism. However, I do feel that my own experience should be of value. We have often spoken of practical details. Students want to know how to determine whether one's voice is carrying in a large auditorium, or how large to write on a blackboard. An experienced teacher can help with such trivia which may loom large before the inexperienced assistant. We discuss problems of cheating, of what control of a class means, how familiar one becomes with students, the role of humor and patience.

I have always hoped that the impact of the seminar would be helping to supply thoughtful teachers rather than technicians trained in educational methods. When the student finally asks 'how?' and 'why?' about topics ranging from a course outline to an item of examination, I am satisfied that an often missing insight has been gained, and I hope that student will be better prepared to face his first class.

READINGS

Baker, J. J. W. (Ed.). 1967. Biology in a liberal education. Publication No. 15. Commission on Undergraduate Education in the Biological Sciences, Washington, D.C.

——1967. Biology for the Non-Major. Publication No. 19. Commission on Undergraduate Education in the Biological Sciences, Washington.

Commission on Undergraduate Education in the Biological Sciences, Panel on Undergraduate Major Curricula. 1967. Content of core curricula

---

[2] CUEBS Publication No. 20, Testing and Evaluating in the Biological Sciences.

in biology. Publication No. 18. Commission on Undergraduate Education in the Biological Sciences, Washington.

Hall, T. S. 1966. How to move a cemetery. *CUEBS News,* 2 (3) : 1–3.

Koppelman, R. 1967. The introductory biology course: its current role in education. *CUEBS News,* 3 (5) : 7–9.

Moment, G. B. 1967. Why biology? a dialogue continued. *CUEBS News,* 3 (4) : 4–5.

Smolker, R. E. 1967. Why Biology? a dialogue. *CUEBS News,* 3 (3) : 1–3.

Stebbins, G. L. 1967. The place of botany in a unified science of biology. *BioScience,* 17 (2) : 83–87.

Thimann, K. V. 1967. General biology teaching. *BioScience,* 17 (2) : 91–94.

D. MODEL COURSE

Teaching Assistants
Teaching to Teach

MILTON HILDEBRAND
Department of Zoology
University of California, Davis

Several years ago I took two of my best TAs to lunch and asked them, "What could this department do to help its TAs become effective teachers?" Although we finished our ice cream without finding a panacea, soon thereafter I introduced a three-unit graduate course titled, "Analysis of the Elements of Effective Teaching of College Biology." The target is the graduate student who will be an assistant professor in a year, or two, or three. The class of about 20 students meets twice a week for sessions that vary between informal lecture and lively discussion. Grading is on a Satisfactory/Unsatisfactory basis.

The content and emphasis of the course are not fixed, but at least there is an outline from which to depart. It goes about like this:

1. What is teaching? What is effective teaching? Objectives of teaching. Unique opportunities and qualities of teaching and learning at the university level. Kinds of teaching.

2. Ways to improve one's teaching.

3. How is teaching evaluated? How should it be evaluated? Objectives and uses of evaluations. Specific instruments. Teaching in relation to research and advancement.

4. Factors influencing learning.

5. The curriculum in biology. Structure according to levels of organization, systematics, significant ideas and concepts, traditional "ologies," special learning experiences, methods and skills. Eclectic programs.

6. The preparation of a course: selection of subject area, objectives, method of presentation, students, and text. Prospectus and outline. Budget. Formal procedures and notices. Detailed schedule.

7. The preparation of a lecture: the lecture as a unit, structure, relation to text and lab, use of notes, timing. Preparation for a lecture: review, practice, facilities. Delivery (each student presents 10 minutes of *his* lecture in a large lecture hall).

8. Examinations: objectives, kinds, characteristics of "good" exams, kinds of questions, arrangement of questions, deriving the desired distribution of scores.

9. Grading: accuracy vs. validity, alternative methods, procedures, recording and reporting.

10. Teaching by discussion: objectives, advantages, preparation, procedures.

11. Teaching in the laboratory: objectives, skills, getting away from lockstep, the use of demonstrations, oral quizzes, practicals.

12. Counseling: objectives, alternative systems, procedures.
13. The creative element in teaching. The rewards for effective teaching.

In addition to these 13 activities each student turns in four of the five following assignments:

Prepare in detail the curriculum in biology at your ideal college.

Prepare in detail the course you would like most to teach.

Prepare in detail one lecture in your course.

Prepare a midterm examination for your course.

Write an essay on any other subject relevant to this course (e.g., evaluation of teaching, nature of teaching-learning process, objectives of teaching, programmed teaching, etc.)

These papers are prepared in draft form prior to discussion of the respective topics in class and are completed after the discussion. References are made available. After the papers are returned, there may be further discussion, students with contrasting points of view being invited to defend their approaches.

The course has had satisfactory, although not enthusiastic, acceptance by the biology departments. Moreover, for 4 years I have been in friendly argument with the Graduate Division and/or the Divisional Committee on Courses over the classification of the course. I mention this because the underlying difference of opinion is basic and is not endemic to this campus. These authorities (or always at least part of one of them, in shifting patterns) want to class the course with teacher-training courses offered in Education, even though it has a different audience and purpose, even though exceptions must then be made in the assignment of credits, and even though it is excluded from that class of courses by official definition. I want the course classed with other graduate instruction in order to avoid the stigma which is (rightly or wrongly) sometimes attached to certain Education courses, and because such classification would acknowledge that teaching and research are two aspects, in equal status, of the same academic profession.

I am not smug about this class. It is difficult to do really well. It is difficult to avoid a taint of presumption. The students do participate freely and do say that they have benefited and are grateful. Still, I would like both students and teacher to stir up more innovation and excitement. Too many graduate students are already deep in academia's mold. They tend to accept "the system" too routinely. The curricula and courses they outline for me tend to be too familiar. This year I shall ask several colleagues with effective and distinctive styles to contribute to the course in the hope of shaking us all off the old familiar baseline.

Realistically, I know that it is too much to expect that the course could make great, or excellent, or even good teachers out of all the raw material that cared to enroll. The objective must be to help all interested graduate students to become better teachers. That, I am sure, can be done, and should be done more widely.

E. MODEL HANDBOOK

Teaching Philosophies, Methods, and Techniques[1]

PHILOSOPHY

This part of the handbook is intended to formulate suggestions for the teaching assistant. The actual teaching methods adopted will depend largely on the type of information to be presented, the desired effect to be achieved (decided upon in consultation with departmental advisor), and the personality of the teacher making the presentation. It is not the intention of this committee to advocate a method to be used, but rather this is left up to the discretion of the teaching assistant. It is hoped, however, that when a question of choice arises, departmental counsel will be sought. For, it is through consultation with experienced professors and clues from the teacher's immediate public that growth and improvement in teaching style and presentation will take place. There is, of course, no one right style in teaching, any more than in painting or writing, and therefore we are not advocating a model in these writings. Yet, as stated in the Report of the Committee on Undergraduate Teaching, "there remains a vast difference between the teacher who has sought and found his own style or voice, perhaps after protracted experimentation and modification, and one who uncritically settles for the way he happens first to teach. For, only in the rare and fortunate instance will a teacher discover his mature style between the gaining of his last degree and the teaching of his first course."

Each new teacher is confronted with many questions that arise in his mind and as a result has many reservations about the responsibility before him. Usually the biggest questions are, what are the desired results and how can I best achieve them? These questions require a great deal of thought and planning to answer, and two teachers applying them to the same class would probably reach different conclusions as to the desired results and methods of approach.

One thing that all good teachers would agree on, however, is that the quantity of knowledge you are trying to impart must be broken down into simpler structured bits so that it can be presented in a logical sequential order. Barzun has put it rather well when he said:

> The teacher must break down the new and puzzling situation into simpler bits and lead the beginner in the right order from one bit to the next. What the simpler bits and the right order are no one can know ahead of time. They vary for each individual and the teacher must grope around until he finds a "first step" that the particular pupil can manage. In any school subject, of course, this technique does not stop with the opening of a door. The need for it goes on and on—as it seems, forever—and it takes the stubbornness of a saint coupled with the imagination of a demon for a teacher to pursue his art of improvisation gracefully, unwearingly, endlessly.
>
> Nor is this a purely mental task. All the while the teacher must keep his

---

[1] Only a small selection from the Teaching Assistant Handbook, University of Utah, is reproduced here as a sample.

charge's feelings in good order. A rattled student can do nothing and a muddled teacher will rattle or dishearten almost any student. The teacher must not talk too much or too fast, must not trip over his own tongue, must not think out loud, must not forget, in short, that he is handling a pair of runaway horses—the pupil and a dramatic situation.

To quote Barzun further,

> How then do you pour a little bit of what you feel and think and know into another's mind? In the act of teaching it is done by raising the ghost of an object, idea, or fact, and holding it in full view of the class, turning it this way and that, describing it—demonstrating it like a new car or a vacuum cleaner. The public has an excellent name for this: "making the subject come to life." The student must see the point, must re-create Lincoln, must feel like Wordsworth at Tintern Abbey, must visualize the pressure of the atmosphere on a column of mercury. The "subject" should become an "object" present before the class, halfway between them and the teacher, concrete, convincing, unforgettable. This is why teachers tend so naturally to use physical devices—maps, charts, diagrams. They write words on the board, they gesture, admonish, and orate. Hence the fatigue and hence the rule which I heard a Dean enunciate, that good teaching is a matter of basal metabolism. The man who yawned during his own lecture was correctly reproved by him who said: "The professor confirms our judgment but usurps our prerogative." And another of the same caliber was neatly told off as "having the facts but not the phosphorescence of learning."

Barzun presents a good case for being properly motivated before presenting subject material to a class. He also is correct in his views that no two people or two groups bring the same background to a learning situation. How then can a teacher assess the appropriate material to present to a learner or group of learners. This takes a good deal of planning on the part of the teacher. If he really desires to do a good job, he will try to evaluate the backgrounds of his students before he structures his material completely or before he decides on the sequence of presentation.

Jerome Bruner has formulated a "Theory of Instruction" which may prove useful to the teacher who desires to know something about the factors that predispose a student to be a learner. His ideas are also very helpful in planning how to achieve the desired results.

What shall a theory of instruction be about? Bruner proposes there are four aspects: *first,* predisposition; *second,* structure; *third,* optimal sequence; and *fourth,* reinforcement and feedback. Let us consider each of these four aspects in a little more detail.

PREDISPOSITION

What are the factors that predispose a student to be a learner? Let us begin with the following simple proposition: that in order to learn to solve problems, it is necessary that alternatives be explored and that you cannot have effective learning or problem solving without the learner's having the courage and the skill to explore alternative ways of dealing with a problem.

It seems that if you take this as the first proposition concerning predisposition, there are three things that immediately can be said. First, that if this is the case, learning in the presence of a teacher, or a tutor, or an instructor should somehow minimize the risks and the severity of the consequence that follows upon exploration of alternatives. It should be less risky for a learner to explore alternatives in the presence of a teacher, than without one present. It is obvious that, at the level of coping with nature in the raw, the person searching for food on his own would stand more risk of eating toadstools and poisoning himself, and hereby bringing exploration to a close.

Yet there are other less obvious things that have to do with the closing down of the exploration of alternatives. *A teacher or parent can instill the fear of being a fool. That can surely paralyze the will to explore alternatives,* for the moment an unreasonable alternative is made to seem like a foolish one, the inner freedom to explore is limited by the requirements of face saving. The encouragement of exploration of alternatives requires some practical minimization of the severity of consequences following exploration.

It seems, further, that one of the ways in which a sense of alternatives to be explored can be opened *is to increase the informativeness of error.* To increase, the informativeness of error essentially involves making clear to the learner what produced a failure; it is not in terms of a characterological analysis but rather in terms of the nature of what it is that he is doing. If you can somehow make the person aware that his attempted answer is not so much a wrong answer, as an answer to another problem, and then get him back on the track, it becomes possible for the learner to reduce the confusion of making the wrong choice.

Still another goal to the exploration of alternatives is through the encouragement of "subversiveness." You must subvert all of the earlier established constraints against the exploration of alternatives. This kind of subversiveness has to do with a healthy skepticism toward holy cows, prefabricated doctrines, and stuffed shirtliness. Let there be no question or doubt that is "not nice to express." The moment you as teachers lose your role as subversives in this respect, you are doing the learner an injustice and yourself an injustice as a teacher.

When we think about predispositions to learn, we have to bear in mind that the very relationship that we have with our pupils is a privileged relationship involving authority and direction; that is to say, the exchange is uneven. We know; they do not. Since that is the case, it becomes very necessary for us not to use this implicit authoritative relationship as a means of using our own office as a way of establishing truth and falsity. It is so easy in the mind of the impressionable person to equate truth with Mr. Smith!

STRUCTURE OF KNOWLEDGE

Now let us turn to the question of the structure of knowledge, its economy, productiveness, and power as related to the capacities of a learner. The first point relates to theorem in the theory of computation proposed by Turing. Turing proposed that any problem that can be solved can be solved by simpler means. That is the theorem. Out of this theorem has come the technology of computing machines. What it says — and it says this only for so-called well-defined problems with unique solutions — is that however complicated the problem, we can break it down into a set of simpler elementary operations.

Now, to move ahead one step, Bruner believes that knowledge about anything can, generally speaking, be represented in three ways, three parallel systems of processing information. One of these is what is referred to as the *enactive representation* of knowledge. How do you tie a running bowline? It is not easy to explain but it is easy to demonstrate. Try to tell somebody how to ride a bicycle, or ski. *It is knowing by doing.* It is the way a child on a seesaw "knows" Newton's Law of Moments. He knows that in order to balance two children on the other side he has to get farther out on his side, and this is the Law of Moments.

Let's look at the second system known as the *iconic representation*. If somebody says, for example, "What is a square?" you might say that you can represent a square *by an image*. It isn't a square, it's an image of a square, and it's a useful image. Many of the things we use in representing knowledge have this iconic property. They have limits, these representing pictures, but let us not run down the importance of these useful images.

Finally, a third way in which knowledge can get represented is *symbolically*. By this method knowledge is represented in words or in those more powerful versions of words, powerful in one way in any case, mathematical symbols. You can turn around the Chinese proverb that one picture is worth a thousand words and for certain purposes one word is worth a thousand pictures. For example, draw a picture of "implosion"; and yet the idea of implosion as such was one of the basic notions that led to the idea of thermonuclear fusion. Implosion is the concept that results from the application of a contrast transformation on the more familiar concept of explosion.

When we speak of the application of Turing's theorem to the question of structuring of knowledge, it is in reference to the representation forms we have been discussing. Early in life and also early in our mastery of a subject we may have to represent things in terms of what we do with them — in much the same way as a child "knows about" balance beams by knowing what to do on a seesaw. We may then emerge with an image of it, however nonrigorous the image may be. Then and only then can language and symbol systems be applied with some degree of likelihood that their reference will be understood. We cannot say anything more important than that. You create a structure, not by starting off with the highest brow symbolic version, but by giving it in the muscles, then in imagery and then giving it in language, with its tools for manipulation. The basic task is to orchestrate the three kinds of representations so that we can lead the person from doing, to imaging what he has done, and finally to symbolization.

Usually in a college catalog when a course is listed, it will say something about a "prerequisite." Any topic also has internal prerequisites in addition to the things that you are supposed to have mastered beforehand. The internal prerequisites may indeed be just precisely the easier modes of representation that get one to a less rigorous, more imageful or enactive grasp of a subject before it gets converted either into ordinary or mathematical language. *The way you get ahead with learning is to translate an idea into those nonrigorous forms that can be understood. Then one can, with their aid, become more precise and powerful.* In mathematics such techniques are called "heuristics." Their use often constitutes a prerequisite to grasping a subject in its full depth. This is most of what is meant when we speak of "spiral curriculum."

OPTIMAL SEQUENCE

With respect to the sequence in which material is presented, different sequences are obviously needed to achieve different objectives. The idea of one right sequence is a myth. You have to be quite clear about what kind of learning you are trying to produce before you can specify what is a good sequence for presenting it. There are sequences that can be described for the production of parrots. We use them all the time. But there is also a sequence that is particularly interesting in that it seems to increase the likelihood that knowledge will be converted into a structure that is economical, productive, and powerful—and therefore transferable. It is worth pausing over.

According to Bruner, if you want to try this method of sequence, then the first thing you might do is to try leading the learner to grasp a structure by induction from particular instances and let him recognize their underlying regularity. If you want the person to transfer his learning to new situations, you had better give him some practice in transfer while he is learning.

The second thing you might try is the use of contrast in your sequence. The fish will be the last to discover water. Economy of representation often makes it necessary for the learner to see the contrasting case. Often concepts are structured in terms of contrast and can only be fully understood in terms of them. To grasp the meaning of commutativity in arithmetic — that $3 \cdot 4 = 4 \cdot 3$ — often may require that we recognize the non-commutativity case of ordinary language. For example, as one little girl put it, "black shoe" isn't "shoe black."

Third, if one wants a sequence that is going to produce powerful learning, avoid premature symbolization. Do not give them that word to parrot before they know what it is about either by manipulation or in images.

Fourth, you might try to give the learner practice at both leaping and plodding. Let him go by small steps. Then let him take great leaps, huge guesses. Without guessing he is deprived of his rights as a mind. We cannot get all of the evidence. It is often by guessing that we become aware of what we know.

Another question related to sequence has to do with what is called "revisiting." Rarely is everything learned about anything in one encounter. Yet we seem to be so impelled to cover, to get through such-and-such period that we forget the obvious point — that the pot is rarely licked clean at one swipe. Perhaps we would do well to take music listening as a model. It is not simply a matter of mastering this subject, or even of converting it into more powerful form. Rather, revisit means an opportunity of connecting what we have learned now with what else we know. Why is such an obvious point so often ignored?

REINFORCEMENT AND FEEDBACK

Instruction is a provisional state that has as its object to make the learner or problem solver self-sufficient. Any regimen of correction carries the danger that the learner may become permanently dependent upon the tutor's correction. The tutor must correct the learner in a fashion that eventually makes it possible for the learner to take over the corrective function himself. Otherwise the result of instruction is to create a form of mastery that is contingent upon the perpetual presence of a teacher.

The will to learn is an intrinsic motive, one that finds both its source and its reward in its own exercise. The will to learn becomes a "problem" only under specialized circumstances like those of a school, where a curriculum is set, students confined, and a path fixed. The problem exists not so much in learning itself, but in the fact that what the school imposes often fails to enlist the natural energies that sustain spontaneous learning — curiosity, a desire for competence, aspiration to emulate a model, and a deep-sensed commitment to the web of social reciprocity.

F. PROGRAMS OF CUEBS CONFERENCES

WASHINGTON CONFERENCE
Sheraton Park Hotel
Washington, D. C.
September 25-26, 1969

WELCOME: Dr. Edward J. Kormondy, Director of CUEBS

PANEL DISCUSSION: *The New College Teacher Reports from the Firing-Line*

Dr. Linda B. Kahan	Antioch College
Dr. Earl H. Meseth	Elmhurst College
Dr. George M. O'Connor	Rockhurst College
Dr. Joseph Ramus	Yale University
Dr. Tod F. Stuessy	Ohio State University
Dr. Donald S. Dean	Staff Biologist CUEBS, Chm.

TALKS BY:

Dr. Stanford C. Erickson, Director
Center for Research on Learning and Teaching
University of Michigan

Dr. Lyle W. Phillips, Director
Division of Undergraduate Education In Science
National Science Foundation

Dr. Richard Harbeck, Chief
Research Training Branch
U.S. Office of Education

GROUP DISCUSSIONS: *How to Improve Preparation for College Biology Teaching*

Chairmen:

Dr. Donald G. Humphrey	Oregon State University
Dr. Edward S. Hodgson	Tufts University
Dr. Johns W. Hopkins, III	Washington University

MICHIGAN CONFERENCE
Rackham Building
University of Michigan
January 8-9, 1970

WELCOME: Dr. Alfred S. Sussman, Associate Dean, College of Literature, Arts, and Science, University of Michigan

On Becoming a College Teacher

Dr. Frank M. Koen, Center for Research in Learning and Teaching, University of Michigan

Problems in the Administration of Teaching

Dr. Erich Steiner, Chairman, Department of Botany, University of Michigan

DISCUSSION:

Dr. Joseph R. Larsen	University of Illinois
Dr. Frederick Forro, Jr.	University of Minnesota
Dr. George H. Kieffer	University of Illinois

WORKING SESSIONS:

A. *Model Program for Making the Teaching Experience a Learning Experience for the T.A.*

Dr. Gerson M. Rosenthal, University of Chicago, Chairman

B. *A Model Program for the Orientation of New Teaching Assistants*

Dr. Michael Forman, Purdue University, Chairman

C. *Alternatives to the Traditional Ph.D. Program*

Dr. Alfred F. Borg, NSF, Chairman

D. *What is the Proper Role of Research in the Preparation of College Biology Teachers?*

Dr. Norman S. Kerr, University of Minnesota, Chairman

Technological Aids to Education

Mr. Hazen J. Schumacher, Jr., Television Center & Center for Research in Learning and Teaching, University of Michigan

BERKELEY CONFERENCE
Lawrence Hall of Science
University of California, Berkeley
February 27-28, 1970

WELCOME: Dr. W. M. Laetsch, Associate Director, Lawrence Hall of Science, University of California, Berkeley

How to Tell the Birds from the Flowers: a critical study of the species *Docturorum de rerum natura studiosorum*

Dr. Walter D. Knight, Dean of the College of Letters and Science, University of California, Berkeley

DISCUSSION:

Dr. Glen E. Peterson	University of Nevada
Dr. Richard A. Dodge	Columbia Junior College
Mr. Stephen K. Webster	Stanford University
Mr. Richard Fluck	University of California, Berkeley

Ph.D. Students in the Biological Sciences Appraise their Teaching Preparation

Dr. Ann M. Heiss, Center for Research and Development in Higher Education, University of California, Berkeley

Possible Solution 1: Education of Teaching Assistants

Selected features of programs undertaken at five institutions followed by discussion from the floor.

Dr. Milton Hildebrand	University of California, Davis
Dr. David O. Norris	University of Colorado
Mr. Robert M. Winokur	University of Utah
Dr. David L. Willis	Oregon State
Dr. Charles G. Wilber	Colorado State

Possible Solution 2: The Case for New Types of Degrees

Dr. Frederick Reif, Department of Physics, University of California, Berkeley

DISCUSSION:

Dr. Sanford S. Elberg	University of California, Berkeley
Mr. William Copeland	University of Oregon
Dr. Kenneth Pike	Arizona State University
Dr. Robert J. Jonas	Washington State University
Dr. A. Lester Allen	Brigham Young University

WORKING SESSIONS:

A. *Model Program for Making the Teaching Experience a Learning Experience for the T.A.*

   Dr. Sanford S. Tepfer, University of Oregon, Chm.

B. *A Model Program for the Orientation of New Teaching Assistants*

   Dr. Loren D. Potter, University of New Mexico, Chm.

C. *Meeting the Needs for College Teachers at Two-year and Four-year Institutions*

   Dr. Stanley E. Gunstream, Pasadena City College, Chm.

D. *Consideration of a Suggested Way to Provide Higher Status for Teaching*

   Dr. Robert Cleland, University of Washington, Chm.

NEW ENGLAND CONFERENCE
New England Center
Durham, New Hamphire
May 7-8, 1970

WELCOME: Dr. Edward J. Kormondy, Director of CUEBS

A Challenge

Dr. Edward S. Hodgson, Tufts University

Where is the Action?: A report of the innovative ideas on preparation of college teachers reported by departments offering Ph.D.-level programs in biology

Dr. Donald S. Dean, Staff Biologist, CUEBS

On Becoming a College Teacher

Dr. Frank M. Koen, Center of Research in Learning and Teaching, University of Michigan

PANEL DISCUSSION: *Alternatives to the Ph.D.*

Dr. E. J. Boell	Yale University, Chm.
Dr. Edward C. Moore	Board of Education, Commonwealth of Massachusetts
Dr. Trevor Colbourn	University of New Hampshire
Dr. Alex Henderson	Millersville State College, Penn.
Mr. Barrett Rock	University of Maryland

Foundation Support for the Preparation of Better Teachers in Higher Education

Dr. Alfred F. Borg	Division Undergraduates Education National Science Foundation, Chm.
Dr. Fred S. Honkala	Division Graduate Education National Science Foundation
Dr. Laura Bornholdt	Danforth Foundation
Dr. Lawrence Friedrich	Division University Programs U. S. Office of Education

WORKING SESSIONS:

A. *Making the Teaching Experience a Learning Experience*
   Dr. G. Fred Somers, University of Delaware, Chairman

B. *A Model Cooperative Intern Program*
   Mrs. Karlene Schwartz, Boston University, Chairman

C. *Guidelines for a Degree for College Biology Teachers*
   Dr. Bruce M. Eberhart, University of North Carolina, Chairman

G. PARTICIPANTS AT CUEBS CONFERENCES

MICHIGAN STATE CONFERENCE

Dr. Robert T. Amborski
Louisiana State University

Dr. Richard V. Bovbjerg
University of Iowa

Dr. Donald S. Dean
Baldwin-Wallace College

Dr. Harvey I. Fisher
Southern Illinois University

Dr. Donald Fluke
Duke University

Dr. Albert W. Grundmann
University of Utah

Dr. Edward S. Hodgson
Tufts University

Dr. Raymond W. Holton
University of Tennessee

Dr. Robert W. Hull
Florida State University

Dr. Donald G. Humphrey
Oregon State University

Dr. Henry A. Imshaug
Michigan State University

Dr. Paul B. Kannowski
University of North Dakota

Dr. Edward J. Kormondy
Director, CUEBS

Dr. Harold W. Manner
St. Louis University

Dr. Stanley D. Musgrave
University of Maine

Dr. J. Bennet Olson
Purdue University

Dr. Thomas G. Overmire
Staff Biologist, CUEBS

Dr. Robert Paterson
Virginia Polytechnic Institute

Dr. J. Arthur Reed
Michigan State University

Dr. G. Fred Somers
University of Delaware

Dr. Charles S. Thornton
Michigan State University

Dr. Carroll A. Swanson
Ohio State University

Dr. R. J. Walstrom
South Dakota State University

Dr. Donald L. Wise
Staff Biologist, CUEBS

Dr. Paul A. Wright
University of New Hampshire

Dr. Newell A. Younggren
University of Arizona

WASHINGTON CONFERENCE

*Recent Graduates

Dr. John Allen
University of Michigan

Dr. Robert D. Appleman*
University of Nebraska

Mr. Major L. Boddicker
South Dakota State University

Dr. Richard V. Bovbjerg
University of Iowa

Dr. Michael M. Brown*
Western Maryland College

Dr. William Davis*
University of Tennessee

Dr. Donald S. Dean
Staff Biologist, CUEBS

Mr. Charles J. Decedue
Louisiana State University

Dr. Sanford C. Erickson
University of Michigan

Dr. Alan Gelperin*
Princeton University

Dr. Richard Harbeck
U. S. Office of Education

Dr. Lester Hearson*
Wabash College

Dr. Edward S. Hodgson
Tufts University

Dr. Johns W. Hopkins, III
Washington University

Dr. Robert W. Hull
Florida State University

Dr. Donald G. Humphrey
Oregon State University

Mr. John R. Jungck
University of Miami

Dr. Linda B. Kahan*
Antioch College

Mr. James F. Kitchell
University of Colorado

Dr. Jerry J. Kollros
University of Iowa

Dr. Edward J. Kormondy
Director, CUEBS

Dr. Edward J. LaRow*
Siena College

Mr. Gordon Leversee
Duke University

Dr. Connie Mannings*
Tuskegee Institute

Dr. Earl H. Meseth*
Elmhurst College

Dr. George M. O'Connor*
Rockhurst College

Dr. Paul D. Olexia*
Kalamazoo College

Dr. Lyle W. Phillips
National Science Foundation

Dr. Joseph Ramus*
Yale University

Miss Lynne Raulerson
University of Georgia

Miss Pamela Roe
University of Washington

Dr. Anthony San Pietro
Indiana University

Dr. Tod F. Stuessy*
Ohio State University

Dr. James G. Townsel*
Virginia State College

Mr. John R. Tripp
Ohio State University

Mr. Robert M. Winokur
University of Utah

Dr. Newell A. Younggren
University of Arizona

GUESTS

Dr. Kenneth E. Eble
American Association of
   University Professors

Dr. Lafe R. Edmunds
National Science Foundation

Dr. Elwood B. Ehrle
Office of Biological Education, AIBS

Dr. John Gillis
Association of American Colleges

Mr. William H. Morris
American Association for
   Higher Education

Dr. Howard Stein
Office of Biological Education, AIBS

Dr. Robert Van Waes
American Association of
   University Professors

Dr. John D. Withers
Staff Biologist, CUEBS

MICHIGAN CONFERENCE

Mr. Gregg Anderson
Indiana University

Dr. Alfred F. Borg
National Science Foundation

Dr. Robert Brandou
Michigan State University

Dr. Robert L. Costello
University of Wisconsin

Dr. Paul Daniel
University of Miami

Dr. Lary V. Davis
University of Notre Dame

Dr. Donald S. Dean
Staff Biologist, CUEBS

Dr. Harold E. Finley
Howard University

Dr. Michael Forman
Purdue University

Dr. Frederick Forro, Jr.
University of Minnesota

Dr. Kerry Garrett
University of Michigan

Dr. Elmer Hadley
University of Illinois-Chicago Circle

Dr. Howard Hagerman
Michigan State University

Mr. Randy Horine
Indiana University

Dr. Robert Hurst
Purdue University

Dr. David Husband
Purdue University

Mr. Jefferey Jackson
The Ohio State University

Mrs. Phyllis Jackson
The Ohio State University

Dr. Norman S. Kerr
University of Minnesota

Dr. George H. Kieffer
University of Illinois

Dr. Frank M. Koen
University of Michigan

Dr. Edward J. Kormondy
Director, CUEBS

Dr. Joseph R. Larsen
University of Illinois

Dr. Georgia E. Lesh
Case-Western Reserve University

Dr. Laurence Levine
Wayne State University

Dr. Robert L. Lowry
University of Michigan

Dr. James A. McCleary
Northern Illinois University

Dr. Kaz Mayeda
Wayne State University

Dr. Thomas R. Mertens
Ball State University

Dr. Jerry J. Nisbet
Ball State University

Dr. Newtol Press
University of Wisconsin

Dr. Fred R. Rickson
University of Wisconsin

Dr. Gerson M. Rosenthal, Jr.
University of Chicago

Mr. Hazen J. Schumacher, Jr.
University of Michigan

Dr. Erich Steiner
University of Michigan

Dr. Lorna P. Straus
University of Chicago

Dr. Alfred S. Sussman
University of Michigan

Dr. Robert Thompson
Marquette University

BERKELEY CONFERENCE

Dr. Dana L. Abell
Staff Biologist, CUEBS

Dr. A. Lester Allen
Brigham Young University

Dr. Doyle E. Anderegg
University of Idaho

Dr. Alfred F. Borg
National Science Foundation

Dr. Robert Cleland
University of Washington

Mr. William Copeland
University of Oregon

Dr. Russell Davis
University of Arizona

Dr. Donald S. Dean
Staff Biologist, CUEBS

Dr. Richard A. Dodge
Columbia Junior College

Dr. William Doyle
University of California, Santa Cruz

Dr. W. T. Ebersold
University of California, Los Angeles

Dr. Sanford S. Elberg
University of California, Berkeley

Mr. Edward Elkin
University of California, Berkeley

Dr. Abe Flexor
University of Colorado

Mr. Richard Fluck
University of California, Berkeley

Dr. Stanley E. Gunstream
Pasadena City College

Dr. Donald R. Hague
University of Oregon

Dr. Robert Harris
University of Arizona

Dr. Ann M. Heiss
University of California, Berkeley

Dr. Milton Hildebrand
University of California, Davis

Dr. Robert J. Jonas
Washington State University

Dr. Anne Kammer
University of California,
Davis

Dr. Walter D. Knight
University of California, Berkeley

Dr. Edward J. Kormondy
Director, CUEBS

Dr. W. M. Laetsch
University of California, Berkeley

Mr. Jeri M. Langham
Washington State University

Dr. John Lattin
Oregon State University

Dr. Howard M. Lenhoff
University of California, Irvine

Dr. Leonard Machlis
University of California, Berkeley

Dr. E. Grant Moody
Arizona State University

Dr. David O. Norris
University of Colorado

Dr. Ingrith Olsen
University of Washington

Dr. Ivan G. Palmblad
Utah State University

Dr. E. T. Pengelley
University of California, Riverside

Dr. Glen E. Peterson
University of Nevada

Dr. Kenneth Pike
Arizona State University

Dr. Loren D. Potter
University of New Mexico

Dr. Gene A. Pratt
University of Wyoming

Dr. W. K. Purves
University of California,
Santa Barbara

Dr. Frederick Reif
University of California, Berkeley

Mr. Larry Ribnick
University of California, Berkeley

Dr. William D. Romey
Earth Science Curriculum Project

Dr. Raymond T. Sanders
Utah State University

Dr. Jay M. Savage
University of Southern California,
Los Angeles

Dr. Harvey Scudder
California State College, Hayward

Dr. Peter Shugarman
University of Southern California,
Los Angeles

Dr. Sanford S. Tepfer
University of Oregon

Dr. Dale Tillery
University of California, Berkeley

Dr. Richard T. Ward
Colorado State University

Dr. Stephen K. Webster
Stanford University, Stanford

Dr. Charles G. Wilber
Colorado State University

Dr. David L. Willis
Oregon State University

Mr. Robert M. Winokur
University of Utah

NEW ENGLAND CONFERENCE

Dr. Milton Adesnik
Columbia University

Dr. Thomas Bannister
University of Rochester

Dr. E. J. Boell
Yale University

Dr. Alfred F. Borg
National Science Foundation

Dr. Laura Bornholdt
Danforth Foundation

Dr. David Botstein
Massachusetts Institute of
    Technology

Dr. Charles Botticelli
Boston University

Dr. Trevor Colbourn
University of New Hampshire

Dr. Joan Creager
Staff Biologist, CUEBS

Dr. Donald S. Dean
Staff Biologist, CUEBS

Dr. Bruce M. Eberhart
University of North Carolina,
    Greensboro

Dr. M. V. Edds, Jr.
Brown University

Dr. Lawrence Friedrich
U. S. Office of Education

Dr. George P. Fulton
Boston University

Dr. Alex Henderson
Millersville State College

Dr. Edward S. Hodgson
Tufts University

Dr. Fred S. Honkala
National Science Foundation

Dr. Evelyn Hurlburt
Montgomery College

Dr. C. Albert Kind
University of Connecticut

Dr. Frank M. Koen
University of Michigan

Dr. Edward J. Kormondy
Director, CUEBS

Dr. Edward C. Moore
Massachusetts Board of Higher
    Education

Dr. Carl R. Partanen
University of Pittsburgh

Mr. Carl S. Pike
Harvard University

Dr. Frank P. Polanowski
Pennsylvania State University

Dr. Gordon M. Ramm
University of Maryland

Mr. Barrett Rock
University of Maryland

Mrs. Karlene Schwartz
Boston University

Mr. William Sharp
Columbia University

Dr. G. Fred Somers
University of Delaware

Dr. Daniel J. Sullivan
Fordham University

Dr. C. Dale Therrien
Pennsylvania State University

Dr. William G. Valleau
University of Maine

Dr. Terry Webster
University of Connecticut

Dr. Langley Wood
University of New Hampshire

H. MODEL FORUM INITIATED BY A GRADUATE STUDENT

College Teaching in Our Curricula

OPENING REMARKS: Dr. Sidney W. Fox, Professor of Biochemistry

ADDRESSES:

THE ROLE OF TEACHING IN THE UNIVERSITY

Dr. Armin H. Gropp
Dean of Faculties
University of Miami

PRE-SERVICE PREPARATION OF COLLEGE BIOLOGY TEACHERS

(A report from a Washington, D. C. conference sponsored by the Commission on Undergraduate Education in the Biological Sciences.)

John Jungck
Graduate student in Cellular
and Molecular Biology

PANEL:

WHAT SHOULD THE ROLE OF LIFE SCIENCE DEPARTMENTS BE IN THE PREPARATION OF COLLEGE AND UNIVERSITY TEACHERS?

Chairman: Dr. Karl H. Muench, Medicine

Members: Dr. S. Greer, Microbiology
Dr. P. V. O. Luykx, Biology
Dr. G. A. Tershakovec, Biochemistry
Mark Skarstedt, CMB
Lorraine Marold, Microbiology
Chuck Moody, Biology
Bill Gehring, Marine Biology

8:00 PM, Monday, November 17, 1969

Commons Building, 1968 Complex, Second Floor
(Access from Dickinson Drive)

Graduate students in CMB, Biochemistry, Biology, Microbiology, and Marine Biology are especially invited. All others welcome.

I. BIBLIOGRAPHY

DAVID L. WILLIS
Oregon State University

Bruner, Jerome S. 1960. *The Process of Education.* Random House, New York. 92 pages.

Roe, Anne. 1952. *The Making of a Scientist.* Dodd, Mead & Company, New York. 244 pages.

Knapp, R. H. 1964. *The Origins of American Humanistic Scholars.* Prentice-Hall, Englewood Cliffs, N. J.

Knapp, R. H., and H. B. Goodrich. 1952. *Origins of American Scientists.* University of Chicago Press, Chicago, Ill.

Knapp, R. H., and J. J. Greenbaum. 1953. *The Younger American Scholar.* Wesleyan University Press.

Gagne, R. M. 1965. *The Conditions of Learning.* Holt, Rinehart & Winston, Inc., New York.

Rogers, Carl R. The Facilitation of Significant Learning. (Paper given at Western Behavioral Sciences Institute, La Jolla, California).

Examination of Educational Testing Service. (Princeton, New Jersey). Pamphlets on testing and evaluating procedures.

Shepherd, Clovis R. 1964. *Small Groups: Some Sociological Perspectives.* Chandler Publishing Co., San Francisco, Calif. 130 pages.

The Excitement and Fascination of Science. 1965. Annual Reviews, Inc. Palo Alto, Calif. (Editor-in-Chief: J. Murray Luck). 566 pages.

Improving College Teaching. 1967. Edited by Calvin B. T. Lee. American Council on Education, Washington, D. C. 407 pages.

The American College. 1966. Edited by Nevitt Sanford. John Wiley & Sons, Inc., New York. 1084 pages.

McKeachie, Wilbert J., and Gregory Kimble. 1965. *Teaching Tips: Guide-Book for the Beginning College Teacher,* 5th ed. The George Wahr Publishing Co., Ann Arbor, Mich. 208 pages.

Mager, Robert F. 1962. *Preparing Instructional Objectives.* Fearon Publishers, Palo Alto, Calif. 62 pages.

Science Education in the Junior College: Problems and Practices. 1966. Edited by Albert F. Eiss. National Science Teachers Association, Washington, D. C. 20036. 53 pages.

The Junior College and Education in the Sciences. 1967. Report of the National Science Foundation to the Subcommittee on Science, Research, and Development of the Committee on Science and Astronautics, U. S. House of Representatives, 90th Cong., 1st Sess. U. S. Government Printing Office, Washington, D. C. 103 pages.

Biology in the Two Year College. April, 1969. A CUEBS Position Paper 26, prepared by Willis H. Hertig, Jr. Commission on Undergraduate Education in the Biological Sciences, Washington, D. C. 20016. 24 pages.

Biology in a Liberal Education. February, 1967. A CUEBS Publication 15, edited by Jeffrey J. W. Baker. (Reports of the Colloquium on Biology in a Liberal Education, Stanford University, August 2-13, 1965.) Commission on Undergraduate Education in the Biological Sciences, Washington, D. C. 20016. 46 pages.

Biology for the Non-Major. July, 1967. CUEBS Publication No. 19. Commission on Undergraduate Education in the Biological Sciences, Washington, D. C. 20016. 80 pages.

Content of Core Curricula in Biology. June, 1967. CUEBS Publication No. 18. Commission on Undergraduate Education in the Biological Sciences, Washington, D. C. 20016. 176 pages.

Testing and Evaluation in the Biological Sciences. November, 1967. CUEBS Publication No. 20. Commission on Undergraduate Education in the Biological Sciences, Washington, D. C. 20016.

Postlethwait, S. N., J. Novak, and H. T. Murray, Jr. 1969. *The Audio-Tutorial Approach to Learning,* 2nd ed. Burgess Publishing Co. Minneapolis, Minn. 55415. 149 pages.

Steps Toward Scientific Literacy. 1967-68. A report of College-Level Conferences on Science for Nonscience Majors. National Science Teachers Association, Washington, D. C. 20036. 22 pages.

Caplow, Theodore, and Reece J. McGee. 1961. *The Academic Marketplace.* Science Editions, Inc., New York. 262 pages.

Also see the bibliography prepared by Dr. Frank Koen on page 42 of this volume. Two worthy additions used by Dr. Donald R. Scoby of North Dakota State in his course are:

Voss, Burton E., and Stanley B. Brown. 1968. *Biology as Inquiry.* C. V. Mosby Co., St. Louis. 239 pages.

Morris, William H. (ed.). 1970. *Effective College Teaching—The Quest for Relevance.* American Council on Education, Washington, D. C. 176 pages. See the bibliography prepared by Stanford C. Erickson, pp. 36–37.

A worthy addition to any bibliography on the subject would be *Memo to the Faculty,* published six times per year by the University of Michigan, Center for Research in Learning and Teaching ($4.00 per year).

Also see Presidential Advisory Committee on Undergraduate Instruction, University of Toronto (1967). *Undergraduate Instruction in Arts and Sciences,* University of Toronto Press, Toronto, 149 pages.

J. RESPONDENTS TO THE QUESTIONNAIRE ON PREPARATION OF COLLEGE BIOLOGY TEACHERS

Department	Institution	Respondent	Number of Ph.D.'s in Typical Year
Biology	Univ. of Alabama	H. S. Schwartz	1
Botany	Arizona State Univ.	James E. Canright, Chm.	4
Zoology	Arizona State Univ.	Shelby D. Gerking, Chm.	5
Biological Sciences	Univ. of Arizona	Newell A. Younggren, Head	9
Botany	Univ. of Arkansas	Lowell F. Bailey, Chm.	2
Biology	Univ. of Arkansas	Perry M. Johnston, Chm.	2–3
Division of Biology	California Institute of Tech.	Robert L. Sinsheimer, Chm.	15
Botany	Univ. of California, Berkeley	Ralph Emerson, Chm.	8
Botany	Univ. of California, Davis	C. Ralph Stocking, Chm.	5
Zoology	Univ. of California, Davis	Herman T. Spieth, Chm.	10
Zoology	Univ. of California, Los Angeles	Albert A. Barber, Chm.	20
Microbiology	Univ. of California, Riverside	Carlton R. Bovell, Vice-Chm.	3
Biology	Univ. of California, Santa Barbara	William K. Purves	11
Biology	Univ. of California, Santa Cruz	Cedric Davern, Chm.	1–2
Botany	Claremont Grad. School	Lee W. Lenz, Chm.	1
Biology	Univ. of Southern California	Bernard L. Abbott, Chm.	9
Biology	Loma Linda Univ.	Elwood S. McCluskey, Associate-Chm.	1
Biology	Stanford Univ.	Richard C. Hanawalt, Director Graduate Studies	12
Botany	Colorado State Univ.	Richard T. Ward, Chm.	5
Zoology	Colorado State Univ.	Charles G. Wilber, Chm.	6
Biology	Univ. of Colorado	Askell Love, Chm.	7
Microbiology	Colorado State Univ.	James E. Ogg, Head	4
Biology	Wesleyan Univ.	Earl D. Hanson, Chm.	2
Biology	Yale Univ.	E. J. Boell, Director Graduate Studies	22
Biological Sciences	Univ. of Connecticut	Frank D. Vasington, Chm.	16
Biology	Univ. of Delaware	G. Fred Somers, Chm.	3
Biology	Catholic Univ.	Dale C. Braungart, Chm.	7
Biology	Georgetown Univ.	George B. Chapman, Chm.	5

J. (Continued)

Department	Institution	Respondent	Number of Ph.D.'s in Typical Year
Biological Sciences	George Washington Univ.	A. H. Desmond, Chm.	2
Microbiology	Georgetown Med. School	Arthur K. Saz, Chm.	3
Biology	Florida State Univ.	Robert W. Hull, Chm.	10
Botany	Univ. of Florida	Leland Shanor, Chm.	3
Zoology	Univ. of Florida	Robert M. Dewitt, Acting Chm.	5
Biology	Univ. of Miami	W. Henry Leigh, Chm.	8–10
Zoology	Univ. of Southern Florida	John C. Briggs, Chm.	3
Biology	Emory Univ.	Robert B. Platt, Chm.	5
Division of Biology	Univ. of Georgia	Donald C. Scott, Chm.	42
Zoology	Univ. of Georgia	Dirk Frauenberg, Acting Chm.	6
Zoology	Univ. of Hawaii	Andrew J. Berger, Chm.	3
Botany	Univ. of Hawaii	Noel P. Kefford, Chm.	3
Microbiology	Univ. of Hawaii	Albert A. Benedict, Chm.	2
Biology	Univ. of Idaho	Doyle E. Anderegg, Head	1
Division of Biology	Univ. of Chicago	Arnold W. Ravin, Associate Dean	22
Biology	DePaul Univ.	Robert C. Thommes, Chm.	12
Biochemistry	Illinois Inst. of Tech.	A. H. Roush	5
General Education in Biology	Univ. of Illinois	George H. Kieffer, Chm.	6
Zoology	Univ. of Illinois	Edward H. Brown	10
Botany	Southern Illinois Univ.	Robert Mohlenbrock, Chm.	4
Zoology	Southern Illinois Univ.	Harvey S. Fisher, Chm.	3–8
Entomology	Univ. of Illinois	Joseph R. Larsen, Head	
Microbiology	Univ. of Illinois	L. Leon Campbell, Head	8
Zoology	Univ. of Illinois	Robert L. Metcalf, Head	6
Microbiology	Indiana Univ.	Arthur L. Koch	2–3
Botany	Indiana Univ.	Anthony San Pietro, Chm.	6
Zoology	Indiana Univ.	Robert W. Briggs, Chm.	12
Biology	Notre Dame	Joseph A. Tihen, Assistant-Chm.	5
Biological Sciences	Purdue Univ.	Henry Koffler, Head	25
Zoology	Iowa State Univ.	Oscar E. Tauber, Chm.	9
Botany	Univ. of Iowa	Robert L. Hulbary, Chm.	3
Zoology	Univ. of Iowa	Richard V. Bovbjerg	6

J. (Continued)

Department	Institution	Respondent	Number of Ph.D.'s in Typical Year
Bacteriology	Iowa State Univ.	William R. Lockhart, Chm.	5
Science Education	Univ. of Iowa	R. E. Yager	5
Biology	Kansas State Univ.	C. Gail Zeller	10
Botany	Univ. of Kansas	Raymond C. Jackson, Chm.	4
School of Biological Sciences	Univ. of Kentucky	Samuel F. Conti, Chm.	4
Zoology	Univ. of Kentucky	Thomas Barr, Chm.	4
Biology	Univ. of Louisville	William S. Davis, Chm.	2
Zoology	Louisiana State Univ.	Kenneth C. Corkum	4
Biology	Tulane Univ.	E. Peter Volpe, Chm.	6
Microbiology	Louisiana State Univ.	M. D. Socolofsky	4
Zoology	Univ. of Maine	Kenneth Allen, Head	2
Botany	Univ. of Maine	Gary A. McIntyre, Chm.	1
Botany	Univ. of Maryland	Robert W. Krauss, Head	4
Biology	Johns Hopkins Univ.	Saul Roseman, Chm.	10
Biology	Boston Univ.	Arthur M. Brads, Science Administrator	9
Biology	Tufts Univ.	Edward S. Hodgson, Chm.	2
Biology	Brandeis Univ.	Attila O. Klein, Chm.	4
Biology	Massachusetts Inst. of Tech.	Boris Magasanik, Head	15
Biology	Clark Univ.	Rudolph F. Nunnemacher, Chm.	2
Botany	Univ. of Massachusetts	David Meyer, Administrative-Assistant	2
Biological Sciences	Smith College	George W. DeVillafranca, Chm.	1
Biochemistry	Univ. of Massachusetts	Henry N. Little, Acting Head	8–10
Microbiology	Univ. of Massachusetts	Robert P. Mortlock	3–4
Zoology	Michigan State Univ.	Charles Stead Thornton, Chm.	8
Botany	Univ. of Michigan	Erich Steiner, Chem.	8
Zoology	Univ. of Michigan	John M. Allen, Chm.	13
Biology	Wayne State Univ.	Stanley K. Gangwere, Graduate Officer	4
Genetics and Cell Biology	Univ. of Minnesota	Frederick Forro, Jr., Head	8
Microbiology	Univ. of Minnesota	Dennis W. Watson, Head	3
Biochemistry	Univ. of Minnesota	Neuman Berger, Administrative Officer	6
Botany	Mississippi State Univ.	George W. Johnston, Head	1
Zoology	Mississippi State Univ.	John T. Morrow, Professor	2

J. (Continued)

Department	Institution	Respondent	Number of Ph.D.'s in Typical Year
Biology	Univ. of Southern Mississippi	George F. Pessoney, Acting Chm.	3
Microbiology	Mississippi State Univ.	Robert G. Tischer, Chm.	1
Botany	Univ. of Missouri	Billy G. Cumbie	4
Zoology	Univ. of Missouri	John Farmer, Chm.	4
Biology	St. Louis Univ.	Harold W. Manner, Chm.	5
Biology	Washington Univ.	Johns W. Hopkins, Chm.	9
Botany and Microbiology	Montana State Univ.	Barton E. Hahn	3
Zoology	Montana State Univ.	D. Cameron, Head	3
Zoology	Univ. of Montana	Albert G. Canaris, Chm.	2
Genetics Institute	Montana State Univ.	Palmer D. Skaar, Director	2
Animal Science	Univ. of Nebraska	Robert D. Appleman	4
Botany	Univ. of Nebraska	Wendell Ganger, Chm.	1
Agronomy	Univ. of Nebraska	D. G. Hanway, Chm.	7
Entomology	Univ. of Nebraska	Earle S. Raun, Chm.	4
Biological Sciences	Dartmouth College	A. E. DeMaggio	2
Zoology	Univ. of New Hampshire	Langley Wood, Chm.	2
Botany	Univ. of New Hampshire	Richard W. Schreiber, Chm.	3
Biology	Princeton Univ.	John Tyler Bonner, Chm.	6
Botany	Rutgers Univ.	David E. Fairbrothers, Acting-Chm.	6
Zoology	Rutgers Univ.	Paul G. Pearson, Chm.	7
Biology	New Mexico State Univ.	William A. Dick-Peddie	3
Biology	Univ. of New Mexico	Loren D. Potter, Chm.	2–3
Biology	Brooklyn College	Mordecai L. Gabriel, Chm.	1–2
Science Education	Columbia Teachers College	Willard J. Jacobson, Chm.	4
Division of Biology	Cornell Univ.	Robert S. Morison, Director	35
Biology	Fordham Univ.	John McLaughlin, Chm.	9
Biology	Hunter College	Richard G. Mawe, Chm.	3
Biology	New York Univ.	James M. Bennett	23
Biological Sciences	State Univ. at Albany	Frederic H. Turscott, Vice-Chm.	4
Biological Sciences	State Univ. at Stony Brook	Charles Walcott, Chm. of the Graduate Committee	4
Biology	St. Johns Univ.	Albert V. Liberti, Chm.	5
Botany	Duke Univ.	T. W. Johnson, Jr., Chm.	5–8
Zoology	Duke Univ.	Donald J. Fluke, Chm.	8
Botany	North Carolina State Univ.	G. R. Noggle, Head	4

J. (Continued)

Department	Institution	Respondent	Number of Ph.D.'s in Typical Year
Zoology	North Carolina State Univ.	David E. Davis, Head	3
Botany	Univ. of North Carolina	Victor E. Greulach, Chm.	8
Zoology	Univ. of North Carolina	Irvine Rey Hagadorn	2
Primate Facility	Duke Univ.	John Buettner-Janusch, Director	3
Physiology and Pharmacology	Duke Med. School	George M. Padilla	4
Biology	North Dakota State Univ.	Donald R. Scoby	5
Biology	Univ. of North Dakota	Marjorie P. Behringer	5
Biology	Univ. of Cincinnati	Frank J. Etges, Director Graduate Studies	4
Biology	Kent State Univ.	Vincent Gallicchio, Coordinator Graduate Studies	5
Botany	Ohio State Univ.	John A. Schmitt, Chm.	3
Biology	Univ. of Toledo	Maimon Nasatir	3
Zoology	Ohio State Univ.	Tony J. Peterle, Chm.	11
Faculty of Science and Mathematics Education	Ohio State Univ.	Robert W. Howe, Chm.	4
Botany	Oklahoma State Univ.	John E. Thomas, Head	3
Zoology	Oklahoma State Univ.	Roy W. Jones, Head	7–8
Plant Science	Univ. of Oklahoma	Frank A. Rinehart	8
Zoology	Univ. of Oklahoma	Cluff E. Hopla, Chm.	5
Agronomy	Oklahoma State Univ.	Ralph S. Matlock, Head	4
Physiology	Oklahoma State Univ.	Calvin G. Beames, Jr.	2
Entomology	Oklahoma State Coll.	D. E. Howell, Head	6
Botany	Oregon State Univ.	J. Ralph Shay, Head	14
Zoology	Oregon State Univ.	Ernest J. Dornfeld, Chm.	7
Biology	Univ. of Oregon	Sanford S. Tepfer, Co-Chm.	6
General Science	Oregon State Univ.	David L. Willis, Chm.	9
Biology	Lehigh Univ.	Saul B. Barber, Chm.	2
Biology	Bryn Mawr Coll.	Robert L. Conner, Chm.	3
Biology	Penn State Univ.	Joseph G. O'Mara, Head	4
Biology	Univ. of Pittsburgh	Carl R. Partanen	7
Biology	Univ. of Pennsylvania	William H. Telfer, Acting-Chm.	9
Division of Biological and Medical Sciences	Brown Univ.	Hubert J. Dyer, Coordinator Graduate Matters	10
Zoology	Univ. of Rhode Island	Robert K. Chipman, Chm.	3
Division of Biology	Clemson Univ.	Rufus K. Guthrie, Director	3
Biology	Univ. of South Carolina	B. Theodore Cole, Head	3
Zoology	South Dakota State Univ.	Robert J. Walstrom, Head	4

J. (Continued)

Department	Institution	Respondent	Number of Ph.D.'s in Typical Year
Biology	Univ. of South Dakota	Webster H. Sill, Jr., Chm.	1
Biology	Peabody Coll. for Teachers	Gus Tomlinson, Chm.	8
Botany	Univ. of Tennessee	Raymond W. Holton, Head	4
Zoology and Entomology	Univ. of Texas	Samuel R. Tipton, Chm.	3
Biology	Univ. of Houston	Glenn Aumann, Chm.	4
Biological Sciences	North Texas State Univ.	J. K. G. Silvey, Chm.	6
Biology	Rice Univ.	Stephen Subtelny, Chm.	7
Biology	Texas A&M Univ.	George M. Krise, Administrative Officer	7
Biology	Texas Technological Coll.	Earl D. Camp, Chm.	1–2
Division of Biological Sciences	Univ. of Texas	Harold C. Bold, Chm.	31
Botany	Univ. of Texas	Billie L. Turner, Chm.	10
Zoology	Univ. of Texas, Austin	A. R. Schrank, Chm.	14
Biology	Texas Woman's Univ.	Kenneth A. Fry, Chm.	5
Botany	Utah State Univ.	Orson S. Cannon, Head	2
Biology	Univ. of Utah	George F. Edmunds, Acting-Chm.	27
Biology	Univ. of Utah	Albert W. Grundmann, Head	10
Botany	Univ. of Vermont	Beal B. Hyde, Chm.	1
Zoology	Univ. of Vermont	Richard W. Glade, Chm.	2
Animal Science	Virginia Poly. Inst.	G. W. Litton, Head	4
Biology	Virginia Poly. Inst.	Robert A. Paterson, Head	5
Botany	Washington State Univ.	Adolph Hecht, Chm.	5
Botany	Univ. of Washington	H. Weston Blaser, Associate-Chm.	5
Zoology	Univ. of Washington	Donald S. Farner, Chm.	5
Zoology	Washington State Univ.	R. A. Parker, Chm.	5
Bacteriology	Washington State Univ.	Herbert M. Nakata, Chm.	3–4
Microbiology	Univ. of Washington	Neal Gorman, Chm.	4
Genetics	Univ. of Washington	Hershel L. Roman, Chm.	5
Biology	West Virginia Univ.	E. C. Keller, Jr., Chm.	3
Biology	Marquette Univ.	Robert G. Thompson	1–2
Botany	Univ. of Wisconsin, Madison	Paul J. Allen, Chm.	8
Zoology	Univ. of Wisconsin, Madison	William C. Burns, Chm.	12
Botany	Univ. of Wisconsin, Milwaukee	Douglas W. Dunlop, Chm.	2
Zoology	Univ. of Wisconsin, Milwaukee	Carroll R. Norden, Chm.	1
Zoology and Physiology	Univ. of Wyoming	George T. Baxter, Acting-Head	2